About

Adam Leigh read English at university and wondered if he would ever be able to write a book rather than just read one. He spent the next thirty years in advertising, trampling on those who got in his way while enjoying a lot of long lunches. He learnt everything there was to know about selling dog food, toilet paper, and the small print on a mortgage ad.

For the last few years, Adam has written extensive topical essays and articles on the foibles of our working lives. *The Curious Rise of Alex Lazarus* is his first novel.

Married to a wonderful wife for thirty years, she is his business partner and most uncritical fan. His three children are less forgiving.

THE CURIOUS RISE OF ALEX LAZARUS

ADAM LEIGH

First published in 2021 by whitefox

Copyright © Adam Leigh 2021

The moral right of Adam Leigh to be identified as the
author of this work has been asserted in accordance with
the Copyright, Designs and Patents Act 1988.

ISBN 978-1-913532-50-5

Also available as an ebook
ISBN 978-1-913532-51-2

Typeset by seagulls.net
Cover design by Jack Smyth
Project management by whitefox
Printed and bound by CPI Group (UK) Ltd, Croydon, CR0 4YY

For Hannah, Sophie, Matthew and Jake

'*AMBITION* is a proud covetousnes; a dry thirst of honour; the long-ing disease of reason; an aspiring and gallant madnesse. The ambitious climes up high and perilous staires and never cares how to come downe: the desire of rising hath swallowed up all his feare of a fall.'

Characters of Vertues and Vices, Joseph Hall (1608)

A **unicorn** is a privately held start-up company valued at over $1 billion. The term was coined in 2013 by venture capitalist Aileen Lee, choosing the mythical animal to represent the statistical rarity of such successful ventures.

Mission:
Family First

Prologue

I can't believe I am here.

A bright April morning and I am in Committee Room 2 in the bowels of the Houses of Parliament. Civil servants are silently laying out pads and pencils, adjusting microphones and straightening chairs. I count twelve name-cards – a veritable dirty dozen of cross-party MPs who will attempt to humiliate me in public.

Somehow, the only thing this reminds me of is Al Pacino in *The Godfather Part II*, whispering in front of the Senate Committee that he is 'taking the Fifth'. Of course, I'm pretty sure I haven't murdered anyone, nor do I have judges and politicians on my payroll to protect me from the inconvenient intrusion of the law. I am most definitely rattled.

Charles, our trusty legal counsel, tells me to stop fidgeting. I sit on my hands for a second and then realise that the nasty flop sweat on my forehead has somehow found its way on to my out-of-the-packet-pristine white shirt. I know I look like a guilty man and I haven't even been asked a question.

You think you've got it all and then your world deflates like a sad balloon. The promise of more money than you will ever need and a crusading charitable foundation, you believe you're on the way to a guaranteed sainthood, or the Jewish equivalent. One small (to your eyes, if not to the media and the political establishment) data breach later and you are vilified beyond comprehension and about to be skewered by a combination of feisty SNP and Liberal Democrat MPs.

I am anticipating a deluge of jealous ignorance and resentment. They are a bunch of digital muppets about to destroy my carefully constructed business. Politicians are undoubtedly fearful of the technology they can't explain to their constituents.

The implications of my imminent ordeal are uncertain. I won't go to prison, I am told, but the censure I will receive may derail my nascent empire, and the fines and lawsuits could mean my future wealth may not necessitate relocation to Monaco quite yet.

Above all, I am afraid that I may not be very good under this pressure. A tendency to not always get to the point, coupled with nervous adrenaline acting as a truth serum, may mean I give away too much involuntarily. Having said that, they will be reliant on an adept stenographer to capture my gabbled answers and will have to work hard to find the revelations among some very tortuously constructed sentences.

I survey the scene with further dismay. My God, the wallpaper is dismal and faded, but not from the sun, as the light is crepuscular and gloomy. The stained-glass window, with the menacing images of a portcullis and an eagle, suggests being pecked to death or ending up in prison. I look at the threadbare carpet and wonder how many of these sessions it has seen. Probably Sir Walter Raleigh thought it had seen better days, too, before he was sent to prison. He had just given us the potato and tobacco and thus can be blamed for the contemporary blights of heart disease and obesity. I have simply blessed the world with a website that makes you a better parent. Maybe one day I will be exonerated and revered?

I feel totally alone. I try not to look behind me at my family in the visitors' section. My anxious wife will be making strained small talk with my worried parents. Mum and Dad would always come to see me in any school performance and celebrate my small roles with enthusiastic pride. This, however, is not my celebrated appearance as Nicely Nicely in *Guys and Dolls* when I was seventeen. Ironically, if you remember his big song 'Sit Down, You're Rockin' the Boat', you will recall the stark line that now seems prescient to my current plight: *The devil will drag you under by the sharp lapel of your checkered coat.* Right now, I am feeling that the world thinks so too. I am not in heaven but entrepreneur's hell.

I glance with indifference for the last time at my beautifully constructed notes and aide-memoire. A cohort of the finest millennial minds have worked without a break for endless days to provide me with uncontentious but often obfuscating answers to the anticipated questions about to be fired my way by the MP for Cleethorpes and his colleague from Colwyn Bay. Stick to the script. Stick to the script. This is the only mantra I have been given to remember. We have role-played, scenario-planned and read tea leaves and cloud formations to prepare for this inquisition. We have even employed a recently retired BBC political correspondent to interview me with his traditional sneering disdain.

But nothing could have prepared me for the unannounced opening of a small door at the back of the room, behind the raised dais on which the table and chairs of the committee are waiting with menace. Can a chair be menacing? Who knows, but when you are that nervous, anything is possible. Out spews the detritus of our political establishment. Seven grey men and five beige women. Elected to office but, to my mind, incapable of presiding over my fate with any real understanding of the complex nuances of my global digital business.

They shuffle into their seats, pour water, get out their notes and nod to one another in complicit anticipation of my imminent execution. I think of the irony of my name in this situation. I will need to rise up from a position of extreme discomfort.

Gordon Hardcastle, Chairman of the House of Commons Cross-Party Communications Committee, clears his throat.

"So, Mr Lazarus. Please can we start by you explaining why you are in breach of European Cookie Law?"

PART 1

STARTING UP

1. Ambition

It all started when I was seventeen.

Perhaps it's an odd way to tell you the tale of my success by beginning in the austere marble edifice of a synagogue on Rosh Hashanah? For those of you not familiar with our religious etiquette, the sermon on the first day of the Jewish New Year is the biggie – the 'State of the Union' or 'Queen's Speech' of our calendar. Full house, infrequent congregants, the rabbi has to make it memorable. We went to a traditional Orthodox North-West London synagogue, where the men sat downstairs, draped in enormous prayer shawls, and the women in a gallery above us, their faces invisible beneath elaborate hats that would not have been out of place at Ascot.

Rabbi Furstein was our minister for many years. A brilliant speaker with a thick Viennese accent and immaculately trimmed goatee, he had fled the horrors of Nazism to spend his life spreading a message of hope and redemption, delivered with a unique blend of wit and accessible erudition. Although over eighty, he stood rigidly upright, proud of the vigorous exercise routine he practised each day before heading off to morning prayers, to keep him young in body and mind.

"*Mein friends*," he would begin each sermon, curling beautifully manicured hands around the corners of the lectern. His command of English was impeccable, but his accent was what I imagined Sigmund Freud must have sounded like when psychoanalysing a patient. He would use his index finger to point, sometimes at the congregation, sometimes to the heavens, trying to draw an invisible thread between the two. That day he wanted to talk to us about ambition.

Rabbi Furstein was a would-be stand-up comic who craved the adrenaline surge of a laughing crowd and was wasted in the religion business. He always started with a joke:

> *"A few years ago, there was a grand announcement in the Birth Section of the* New York Times. *Maybe you remember it? 'Mr and Mrs Marvin Faigenbaum are delighted to announce the safe arrival of their 8lb 6oz beautiful son on July 26, Dr Jonathan Faigenbaum.'"*

The congregation chortled in self-recognition. Jewish communities are collectively driven by an aspiration for progression, perhaps the result of our persecution or the fact that we are not very good at sport. The rabbi acknowledged this as he progressed.

> *"Well, I am sure you have heard the joke before, but it does reveal our need to succeed. Which of you does not want their children to do well? Which of you can honestly say that you have not wanted a new possession, a better job, a nicer house? You don't have to tell me the truth, but I know the real answer. Fear not, I have good news for you all. Judaism has no issue with individual ambition, it just has to be contextualised within our duty to live life with Torah at its heart. The Tenth Commandment states: 'You shall not covet your neighbour's house. You shall not covet your neighbour's wife, or his male or female servant, his ox or donkey, or anything that belongs to your neighbour.' It doesn't prohibit the aspiration of wanting your own belongings. After all, who wouldn't want a nice ox or donkey? As long as your reasons are positive and not fuelled by envy, you most definitely have the Lord's blessing. Also, don't forget to feed them regularly.*

> *"Did you know that in Hebrew the word for ambition is 'Shaiyf'? Its etymology is curious as it means 'ambition, aspiration and striving' but also, more surprisingly, 'inhalation and breathing', which is a very different thing. Now, why would this be? Mein friends, let me suggest something to you.*
>
> *"We exist to strive for self-betterment. We are meant to study, to learn and to move forward by improving our knowledge of the world around us to make us better people within our families and communities. It is why we exist. And of course, to exist, you have to breathe. The oxygen in our lungs is the life force that allows us to remain restless in our individual quest to be a better, nicer and wiser person each day."*

Rabbi Furstein was nothing if not thorough in his sermons. There followed many examples from centuries of Talmudic debate suggesting that ambition was sometimes acceptable and sometimes not, depending on the rabbi, the day of the week and who was asking. Half an hour later (those sermons weren't short), he concluded with a challenge to the congregation, delivered with an impish smile.

> *"So, I ask you, what more are you going to do? What are you going to do for each other? What are you going to do for the community? What more are you going to do for the world? Ambition is a fine thing, don't let anyone tell you otherwise. Just do more good things in its pursuit."*

I suspect I didn't really pay much attention at the time. I was seventeen, my mind was filled with thoughts of girls, football and which university I might go to. But when we got home for lunch, all hell broke loose between my father and grandfather, their different perspectives and values brought to the fore by the rabbi's well-intentioned sermon.

My father, Stuart, is an academic of some repute. A professor of political history at a leading London university, he is also a well-known media commentator and speaker on the corporate circuit. His published works focus on the intersection of technology with political systems. In particular, he has written extensively on the Industrial Revolution. His reputation was cemented by his biography of Ned Ludd (*The March of Progress and the Machine Breaker*), who, as the founder of the Luddites, smashed the textile machines of the late eighteenth century to protect the livelihoods of the manual workers they were replacing. My father argued that the liberation of technology did not necessarily protect the core values of a healthy society. His mealtime debating nemesis was his own father, Manny.

Zayde ('Grandpa' in Yiddish, if you're wondering) came to London as a baby from Minsk in Russia in 1910 with his family, who were all milliners. His father made hats for the religious men of the East End, fedoras and trilbies, and Zayde left school at fourteen to learn his trade in a St Mark Street workshop, behind Petticoat Lane. When he returned from national service, he realised that having survived fighting the Nazis, he was more determined than ever to rely only on his own efforts. Knowing he would do great things, he married my grandmother, produced my father and, most crucially, decided to expand the family business to retail.

In 1947, he opened Feltz's Felts & Fedoras at the top of Stamford Hill, and over the next few years seventeen more shops followed. In the '60s he shortened the name to just Feltz's and started making ladies' hats too. He sold trilbies and caps wholesale to a range of stores including Burton and M&S, and his 'cloche de Paris' was a winner with Dorothy Perkins for many years. Hats, of course, became less ubiquitous, and by the '80s he had just two shops, which eventually shut down. Sartorially speaking, the growing breed of new yuppies did not feel the need for a head covering.

Nevertheless, he retired a wealthy man with a big house in Hampstead Garden Suburb and a bolthole apartment in Florida. He educated his two children privately and created a nest egg of capital to do the same for his five grandchildren. My father's brand of academic socialism did not preclude his commitment to me and my sister, Judith, and we both attended highly regarded independent schools. But my relationship with my grandfather was far more significant than just being a beneficiary of his largesse. He was my inspiration for believing in the need to achieve material success.

He would school me in homespun Yiddish aphorisms that articulated an approach to life in which we should strive for more. I was more excited hearing him tell me about the thrill of getting keys to a new shop than seeing my father's joy as he unpacked a pristine copy of his latest book. I would listen assiduously to Zayde's stories of bamboozling dozy fashion buyers to secure a significant new order, and glaze over when my father enthusiastically outlined the syllabus of a new course he was teaching. When I was fourteen, Zayde had taught me the difference between turnover and gross profit. At the same time, if Dad tried to explain why I needed to rail against the Thatcherite dismantling of a unionised workforce, I would become a truculent and morose teenager. He'd immediately give up and turn (with some success) to my more receptive younger sister.

That lunchtime, galvanised by a sermon about aspiration, battle lines were drawn between father and son, with voices slowly rising as their respective positions were outlined. My future was the focal point of the debate. I had mentioned my indecision about university choices and for some reason it had unleashed pent-up tension between them.

"Sure, Alex should go to university," my grandfather shouted as he waved his fork around and unwittingly dislodged a piece of roast chicken, which fell on his lap. "But he is going to learn less about life there than he would working in a shop serving customers for a couple of months."

My father was having none of it.

"Listen, Dad. You have no concept of him pursuing knowledge for its own sake and his betterment. I know my son. He is naturally curious. He loves to understand why things are as they are."

"I know your son better than you. He wants to make money. He wants to run a business."

My father was now turning tomato-red in frustration with what he saw as his father's immigrant attitude to wealth accumulation. "You are wrong. I will bet you this house that he ends up not just studying but using his learning for the improvement of others."

It seemed an excessive gesture and it clearly riled his father. "You are betting the house I paid for?" My grandfather was very generous, but also liked to remind everyone of his philanthropy.

"Is that relevant?"

"Well, look at you, Professor Moneybags. Your book-writing pays nothing, and your teaching hardly makes much of a contribution." It was a hurtful and unnecessary comment. My father slammed his fist on the table and a couple of roast potatoes leapt a few inches off his plate in unison. It was at this point that I felt I had to try to engender a spirit of family reconciliation.

"Please can you not debate me like I'm not here? Why does it matter what my ambitions are? I'm seventeen and haven't even passed my driving test. I'll sort my own life out, don't you worry."

This seemed to do the job and a begrudging silence descended over the sounds of scraping plates. My father, muttering to himself, left the room to get some more wine. A mischievous grin spread across my grandfather's face.

"Now that Trotsky is out the room, tell me the truth, Alex. Which is it: make a million by the time you are thirty or write a book about some *verkakte* prime minister from two hundred years ago?"

"Zayde, it's a no-brainer. I'll take the cash." He may have been over eighty, but he understood me, it seems, better than my father.

My mother and sister were far more thoughtful about the sermon when we adjourned for some tea and cake. I have perhaps created a picture of a traditional patriarchy in our family, but that is most definitely not the case. My mother, Ruth, is a very highly regarded psychotherapist, with a particular interest in the relationship between self-esteem and anxiety, and she too is a published author. What differentiates her from my father and his love of arcane political theory is that her outlook is grounded in everyday common sense and wisdom. To make something of yourself, you have to believe in your positive attributes. To understand what those are, you have to be prepared to be truthful about what you can and can't do. In response, therefore, to my father and grandfather bickering over my future, she quietly offered her view a little later.

"You know, boys, you've got it all wrong."

"Unlikely," Zayde said, dunking some honey cake into his tea.

"How so?" my father added.

"Well, you're making it a binary choice for Alex. His ambition will be either to write a book or be the next Richard Branson."

I tried to intercede, worried that another battle was imminent. "Hello. I am sitting here. I thought we'd dropped this subject?"

"Alex will be the sum of many parts," my mother continued. "His ambition will be fluid. He'll have conflict and he'll make big changes along the way. He's a mixture of all of us and he'll be torn between the desire to do right and the need to do well. He'll fail as much as he succeeds."

"I'll take your word for it, Mum, but I do wish you'd all stop telling me what I'm going to do. Right now, a farm in Australia is looking an attractive choice if it means getting away from you lot."

The men looked a little contrite, but were also clearly dissatisfied that the argument had fizzled out into a draw without an outright victor.

By this point, my sister, then fifteen, was a little bit put out. She was far cleverer than me, better at sport, and a much nicer person, not that I would have admitted it to anyone.

"If you are telling everyone's fortune, what's my future?"

My mother gave her an affectionate squeeze and, in an act of female solidarity, simply said, "You, my darling girl, you are going to do something worthwhile and make a proper success of your life."

As ever, my mother was right about everything.

2. The Meeting

My wife, Sarah, was heavily pregnant with our second child when it all began. I was sitting on a park bench, enjoying momentary respite from slides, swings and monkey bars. My two-year-old was blithely eating the contents of a sandpit, oblivious to my watchful presence. This was parenting at its best. Coffee in hand, no physical exertion required, and a gated sandpit creating a temporary desert prison. The occasional words of encouragement lobbed in his vague direction were the extent of my care.

It was particularly hot, that summer of 2012. Sarah was not happy being pregnant in the airless nights and, with selfless magnanimity, I would rise as the first light of dawn awoke our energetic Theo. Surrounding ourselves with toys and games, I would start with the best intentions of assiduous mental stimulation for my inquisitive toddler, until the lure of Sky Sports proved too great and we would embark on a more meaningful education on the Premier League, based on the goals compilation of the 1996–97 season. It's amazing how his request for 'more igsaw' could sound like 'Can I watch Shearer's hat-trick against Bolton?' to the untrained ear.

I was continually tired, my energy sapped by the cloying heat of those long muggy days. With another child only weeks away, I was very excited and secretly desperate for a little girl to complete the symmetry of my perfect young family. This was going to be a transitional moment in my life, the point at which things got serious. Fourteen years of unchecked ascent in various advertising agencies meant a certain amount of superficial kudos, a steady income, but also a feeling of restless dissatisfaction that I was answerable to someone else. I was desperate for some change.

I was engulfed in aimless daydreaming as Theo patted a large sandcastle with an increasingly Norman-Bates-like frenzy. Sadly, it was not his, thereby causing much wailing from an innocent fellow sandpit prisoner.

"Theo, that's not your castle," I shouted to no one in particular as I took another slurp of coffee, followed by a flurry of increasingly hopeless pleas.

"Theo. Put down the spade!"

"Theo, watch that little girl's eye!"

"Theo, pull up your pull-up!"

"Theo, I am not clearing that up!"

As I sat motionless, too weary to intercede, I became aware that someone had appeared next to me, and I glanced left to see a fellow father, coffee and paper in hand, equally reluctant to participate in 'sandageddon'.

"I wouldn't worry, she's had worse shoved in her mouth by her older brother," he ventured cheerfully. Slightly flummoxed with embarrassment, I replied, "Oh, I'm so sorry, is that your daughter? Theo's normally so docile. I think he may have been deranged by the sun."

"You enjoy your coffee. Honestly, I'm not being sarcastic. I have every intention of reading each word of the sports section in this paper, even if your son buries her alive."

"Don't worry. He's not done that to anyone for weeks."

"Why do I think it would be better if their mothers were here?" he asked.

"You have a point. My wife always says that I'm good at running around and being physical, but I haven't got the patience to worry about how his mind is actually developing."

"My wife is even more specific. She says the only thing the children will learn from me is how to absent themselves from domestic responsibility."

I rarely chat to strangers in parks and had certainly never embarked on such an in-depth analysis of parenting skills with someone by choice. I felt the need to introduce myself formally.

"I am Alex. Theo is two and I have another one due in four weeks." I sounded like I should be in a playgroup and the sentence should have been sung, accompanied by hand actions.

As if reading my mind, my new playdate replied in kind: "I am Sam I am, and my child in a mess, well, she's called Bess."

"Impressive."

"Actually, I'm Julian and my daughter's Phoebe, but I wanted to pretend that I had actually been to a playgroup."

We chortled, clearly deciding that the conversation was worth continuing, especially as the children were now calmly ignoring each other, having found new sand tools to use incorrectly. Seemingly more comfortable talking about our professional lives, I told him about my role as managing partner for a leading digital advertising agency, and he in turn explained that he was a senior associate working for a media-specialising West End law firm. We lived near one another and he was a child ahead of me as he awaited the arrival of his third. His wife was a management consultant and mine a GP.

What was unusual was how quickly we started confiding our respective frustrations with the constraints of not working for ourselves. He told me he had a couple of small businesses on the side, a property company and a stake in a nightclub. I, in turn, admitted that I was always writing business plans for random ideas. I just hadn't found the right partner to discuss them with.

By the time we adjourned to the park's café to buy the children an ice cream, we had somehow elicited from one another the admission that we wanted to do something entrepreneurial with our lives and take a bit of a risk. I was genuinely beguiled by his charm and confidence. He had an effortless poise and the silent arrogance of a gilded boarding school education (Harrow, it transpired). All this as we wiped melted Cornetto stains from our children's sandy and sweaty clothes.

When my son proceeded to fill his nappy with a bowel movement that could be heard in France, I knew it was unfortunately time to go.

"Well, this fabulous parent needs to return home and hose his child down."

"Wouldn't it be good if we actually were fabulous parents?"

"I sometimes wish I could go online and someone would do it all for me."

"That would be a good business, wouldn't it?"

"Especially if it did birthday presents."

And then there was silence. A silence that was resounding and prophetic. A silence that portended an imminent change in our lives. OK, that is probably a slightly bombastic recollection of a momentary lull in the conversation, but I am pretty certain we paused for thought. All that career chat, all that hard child supervision and, above all, the bravado of describing our self-belief that we could achieve more. I spoke first. It is relevant, because before we get into all the details, I want you to know that it was most definitely my idea.

"You know what, Julian. There really isn't a decent parenting website that does anything clever. It's all nappy rash advice and how to stop tantrums. I bet there's a huge opportunity out there?"

The idea was flimsy and vague. But on that sunny day, as I held my foul-smelling and filthy child, I wondered why no one had tried to commercialise the concept of competent parenting. I desperately wanted to carry on the chat but knew that the practicalities of actually being a parent had interceded and I had to go home.

Julian seemed very engaged and equally disappointed to curtail the conversation. I therefore suggested that we reconvene as soon as possible to explore the potential. Like putative lovers, we swapped numbers and agreed to go on a first date, albeit as platonic would-be entrepreneurs.

* * *

Julian and I arranged to meet for a drink a week later. After ordering at the bar, we sequestered ourselves at a discreet corner table to have some privacy so I could pitch my idea to him. I had chosen my outfit carefully, shaved and anointed myself with a variety of lotions. It was a strange thing to do before a business meeting, but clearly, deep down, I felt the need to make a good impression.

Since our encounter in the park, I had stayed up late researching and scribbling notes in an elegant Moleskine notebook that I had rushed out to buy, signifying the beginning of a new chapter. The idea had grown rapidly in my feverish excitement. Initially, I wondered if we should just start an e-commerce business. But the more research I did, the more I wondered if I had alighted on a brilliant idea that had not been delivered before. There was, of course, a plethora of parenting sites, but they were communities of self-supporting advice, often sponsored by nappy brands or retailers. To my mind, they were resolutely prosaic and practical, lacking magic and emotion.

Why was I intent on pitching an idea to someone I met in a park? It was hardly the most considered decision and perhaps he wasn't who he said he was. Maybe he was a male nanny who, as a pathological liar, had filched the persona of his employer to make his trips to the swings more exciting? Or, more alarmingly, he was who he said, but was an incompetent business brain, a feckless chancer without an ounce of gravitas or substance.

Strangely, I wasn't worried. I am instinctive and believe that first impressions are inherently accurate, and I saw in Julian a persuasive charm and sense of entitlement. Plus, like me, he complained about the limitations of his employment. Everyone else I knew seemed to be rooted to a career trajectory that was linear and unbending. I was ready for a grand career statement.

I had thought a lot about what I was going to say to him and was nervous about his reaction. Fuelled by a sip or two of alcohol, I jumped straight in.

"So, Julian, how about we jack in our jobs, risk our steady incomes and launch a start-up based on being a better parent?"

"No 'how are you'? No foreplay? Blimey, you don't hold back."

"What can I say? An afternoon in a sandpit with you and I am putty in your hands."

He sipped his pint and was silent.

"In all seriousness, are you actually serious?" he eventually asked.

"I really am. I've done a lot of thinking since we met. It struck me that though we joked about our parental incompetence when we were chatting, we are after all the epitome of the modern engaged father. We have busy lives. Our wives have successful careers and we are more anxious about our kids and certainly more involved than our parents were in the minutiae of their lives. True?"

"Well, certainly true of my father. He spent time in prison for insider dealing." I let this comment go as I was on a roll and, besides, who can say if dishonesty is hereditary.

"How much would you pay to be a better parent?"

"Is there really a price to be put on the love of your children?"

"What if I told you that for about £3.50 a month, I am going to get you a place in the Parenting Hall of Fame. What would you say?"

"I'd say there's no such thing and £3.50 seems a very arbitrary figure."

"Fair enough, but let me tell you why we are going to be famous. There is lots of free advice online. You can engage in a conversation about how to deal with chapped nipples and which papoose is best for your back."

"I was in a chat room with someone called Keith discussing the very same, only the other day."

"But surely what really matters is not opinion but being able to deliver the goods. The best presents, the best products and the best experiences."

"Go on."

"It's Phoebe's birthday. She loves princesses and snakes. You want to have a princess snake0-charmer party entertainer and buy her a Cinderella costume that isn't highly flammable and made by little children on the other side of the globe. You want chocolate snakes for the party bags. Our site will allow you to search against these requests and create a bespoke package for you. One click of your shopping basket and you'll have everything sorted."

Julian was now staring at me with alert intent. Did I say he had lovely eyes?

"We will be not a community but a subscription site that allows you to search against random and eclectic criteria, like the wishes and whims of our children. We'll deliver experiences and opportunities that'll make £3.50 a month seem like the bargain of the century."

I paused for a moment for dramatic effect.

"We will become a marketplace for childhood. You'll get access to offers for kid-friendly hotels, you'll be able to go to special screenings of Disney films, you'll be able to create unique parties, you'll even be able to get access to regulated childcare, tutors and ballet teachers."

"Is it easy to build? How will you recruit enough offers and services to make it worthwhile? You make it sound so easy, Alex."

"Trust me, the answer is yes to both. We just have to identify what people want to search for and match it to a solution. Plus, we're going to create some very unique experiences."

"You're very certain, which means either you're very smart or I'm very stupid believing you. Why on earth do you want a lawyer as partner for this venture?"

"Fair point. I mean, you could be just some random bloke I met in a park."

"I am a random bloke you met in a park. As it happens, though, I'm bloody well-connected."

I banged the table with more force than was necessary.

"That's why. I want someone who can help me bring the money in and who can deal with the commercial challenges we're going to face. We're going to license and produce content. We're going to have lots of commercial agreements. I'm good at the big picture. I suspect I will skim a long contract a bit too often. You understand the entertainment and the digital landscape from a commercial perspective. I've built digital platforms for big businesses and know a lot of long-haired blokes from strange places who can write code. What could go wrong?"

"You're serious about this idea, aren't you?"

I put my hand on his shoulder with as much sincerity as such a gesture would allow.

"You bet. I think this can be huge. I think we can monetise our need to be better parents but with the efficiency and speed of the digital age." The words hung in the air for a moment. I realised I was sounding like a bad business self-help book with too much jargon. He seemed to love the clichés, and we clinked beer glasses with the gusto of feasting Vikings.

"Here's to *somethingparent.com* then. Have you thought of a name? Did inspiration come to you late last night in your study?"

"The loo, actually." Julian flinched at this reference.

"So, I have conducted a very significant branding exercise among a sample that included my GP wife and her mother, who happened to be in the kitchen at the time."

"And?"

I did a fake drum roll on the table. I may even have hummed a few bars of Beethoven's Fifth for added mood-setting. Then, with as much dramatic flourish as I could muster, I turned over a piece of A4 paper, and written in large Gill Sans type (after much serious font-searching) was the name:

PrimaParent.com

Julian seemed ambivalent. "Is it any good? he asked, clearly un-convinced.

"Live with it for a day or two. It's short. It alliterates. It suggests 'first' – i.e., you are the best. And it only costs £40 to register."

"All right. I'll ask my mother-in-law what she thinks too. She'd be mortified if she thought this was all down to yours. I am genu-inely very excited about this, I really am. We need to discuss it properly and at length."

Of course, I'm abbreviating the conversation. I had prepared a fuller technical presentation in anticipation of seducing him with my initial sales pitch, including the different search algorithms that might also be the basis of this site, and it certainly was a very quick decision to progress. It was 2012, not the failed dot-com boom of 2000, and just to give you some context, Facebook already had a billion users. We were not at the beginning of a revolution but in the middle of an age of limitless potential. If that sounds a bit over-simplistic, all I can tell you now is that for the first time in my working life I had an unshakeable resolve to work only for myself and not be an employee. The horizons of my future expanded and I envisioned glorious success, oblivious to any obstacles that could be encountered.

We mapped out a series of meetings and the topics we needed to cover – from creating the product to building it and establishing a launch. Above all, we had to decide about its funding and the basis of our partnership. We needed some proper time off work for these discussions and realised that our imminent paternity leave could be used to carry on the conversation. The irony of undermining our support period for our spouses to plan how to make money from parenting was not lost on us. But as long as we did our bit, surely we could snatch some downtime to use for constructive business planning?

And we were off.

3. The Team

A month after meeting Julian in the pub, my daughter, Emily, was born, and I was engulfed by a tidal wave of exhaustion. Theo, excessively disgruntled by the entry of a rival in the family, decided that the best response to sharing the limelight was to create poo mayhem. Eschewing his growing reputation as a potty-trained prodigy, he endeavoured to defecate as often as possible, but only in the most inconvenient places he could think of: his cot, the fruit and veg aisle in the supermarket and – his personal *poo de résistance* – the pool one Sunday morning at our local gym.

I took my allotted two weeks' paternity leave and was very happy four days after my happy news when I received a text from Julian with the terse message: *Sam has arrived. Whole new world of sleeplessness.* I promptly replied: *Business planning in a coffee shop ASAP?* He replied instantaneously: *Pleeeease.*

There was the small matter of discussing with Sarah my embryonic business idea now that our most recent embryo was screaming with gusto and an impressive relentlessness. I had mentioned that I was considering a business idea with my new friend from the park when I went to meet Julian in the pub before Emily's birth. Sarah had not really been too engaged in the conversation, mildly miffed that I would not be massaging her rather swollen feet in front of the telly.

What about Sarah, who will have a significant but unwanted part in this narrative? You are going to like her lots more than you like me. We met in our final year at university and she has always been the perfect partner to smooth over the volatility of my needy personality. A GP in a local practice, she is adored by her patients and colleagues alike and does a host of additional voluntary work, particularly in providing counselling and emotional support to the wider community. Her altruism has allowed me to embark on a single-minded quest for personal glory. As will become apparent, there were many moments when her selflessness was strained by my lapses in paternal duty. Think of her as a sort of potty-mouthed Mother Teresa.

The single-minded pursuit of an aspiration – by definition, a selfish quest for glory – can create unintended casualties. I was about to put that theory into practice by goading a kindly soul whose ambition could only be measured through the volume of people she quietly helped.

Timing being everything, I chose my moment carefully to tell her that I was seriously thinking of abandoning a reasonable salary to live on her paltry GP's stipend and our collective savings. She was delirious and depleted with exhaustion, so I was making her a treat of breakfast in bed. A bit suspicious, given that I'd only done this once before in our entire relationship and we'd never managed to get the Bircher muesli stain out of her favourite linen.

Chomping in a zombified state on a piece of toast as Emily finally slept soundly beside her, she stared blankly at the wall, unable to focus her eyes on me.

"So, you remember Julian?" I casually ventured.

"No. Who's that?"

This was going to be a bit trickier than I had anticipated.

"You know, the guy I met in the park and then went for a drink with."

"What about him?"

"He's just had his third."

"His third what?"

"Child."

"What did he have?" she asked with not unreasonable indifference, given she had never met him.

"A boy called Sam." I realised that he had actually just told me the name, not the sex. "Or a girl called Sam. Definitely one or the other."

She smiled reflexively. She couldn't have been less interested.

Leaping to my feet with unnecessary theatricality, I started to pace the bedroom and deliver a short speech I had rehearsed on the toilet some ten minutes previously.

"Anyway, I'm thinking of going into business with him to launch a new parenting website. We've had a really interesting idea and we're going to write a plan and see if we can get some funding. I've come to the conclusion that, unbelievably, nobody is doing this properly. I know it's odd timing, but you've always encouraged me in whatever I want to do. Well, I think now is the chance to do my own thing. You know I've been so frustrated working for someone else. I've never been more excited to have met someone who I really think might be a great counterbalance to my skills. Do you believe me, that I can create something for myself?"

I stared at my shoes, having delivered this rather florid speech (although I have to say I think I nailed it), and my heart beat a little faster, because I wouldn't have wanted to upset Sarah for anything. Silence. I was too scared to look up.

"Well, say something, please."

But Sarah couldn't say anything because she had fallen asleep, and a piece of granary toast and marmalade was stuck to her forehead. I carefully peeled it off and cleaned her sticky face with a Pampers Extra Sensitive wet wipe. I couldn't have loved her more at that moment, as she and our gorgeous daughter breathed peacefully in synchronised unison.

"I'll take that as a 'yes' then, and I'll be sure to keep you updated," I whispered as I edged out of the room.

* * *

Julian and I met, as often as we could flee our parenting responsibilities, at Manuela's, a local Mexican café with a menu based on creative ways to smash an avocado. Our conversations were very focused, due to the shortage of time, and we set clear goals. Early on, we divided up the plan as follows: site construction, functionality, technical spec, marketing and acquisition – that was my remit and experience; company structure, funding, P&L forecasts, growth strategy – Julian ploughed into these with enthusiasm.

Our meetings continued with regularity as we went back to work. We would try to find moments of temporary calm each evening to speak and would carve out as much time at the weekend as was practical. This was not sustainable, and we knew we had to quickly commit to this project if we believed in its potential. One Sunday morning in early October, sitting at our favourite table in Manuela's, Julian announced with mock solemnity that it was time to escalate our plans.

"We need to go to the next level."

"Julian, I am not moving in with you." He ignored me, but I suspected for the first time that my wisecracks might be beginning to grate.

"We can't sit here much longer pontificating. We need bums on seats and names on spreadsheets. If we don't recruit a great team, we might as well settle up for the coffee and carry on our jobs."

"I am not doing that," I said forcefully. "I've checked out and I think they've noticed. If I carry on like this, I'm going to have to ask Manuela for a job smashing the avocados."

"Right then," he replied, stretching his fingers and cracking his knuckles as if preparing to perform delicate surgery, "do you know anyone vaguely competent?"

"What do you take me for? My little black book is awash with competence."

"How quaint. You still use paper." Already it was clear – he loved having the last word in any debate with me.

* * *

It's hard to achieve global success on your own. We had to actually persuade some people to sign up quickly to our vision and take a risk with us. Indeed, we knew we needed a team to give credibility to our initial investor presentations. We identified our immediate priorities that day. We needed to recruit a core team of three people straight away. Our first priority was a CTO (chief technical officer), our genius who could build this and make it work. We also had to have a good finance director in place to help us forecast growth, calculate its cost, and manage the money for us carefully while ensuring sufficient governance for our investors. Finally, we wanted an experienced operations director, someone to shout at us all and make things happen by producing complicated spreadsheets explaining who was doing what by when.

We would also recruit some gullible, malleable interns to do endless amounts of work for as little as we could pay them. Fooled by naive optimism that they'd have the opportunity for imminent success, they would be sustained by a lot of free food and alcohol to mask this modern version of capitalist slavery.

Julian quickly found a potential finance director. Remember I mentioned that he had a small stake in a nightclub? His school-friend Barnaby Something-Something had bought a run-down wine bar and relaunched it as Soirée, and Julian had put some seed money into the project. The club had gained traction when it was used as the venue for the incredibly popular reality TV show *So I Want to Marry an Heiress*, in which a succession of men from different social backgrounds go on stilted dates with an array of boarding-school-educated beauties, united only by their trust funds and magnificent dowries. There were seven partners who owned Soirée and Julian wanted to introduce me to Simon Rees, whom he described as 'the coolest accountant you will ever meet'.

I had the mindset that Julian and I needed to trust each other completely and, with so much to do so quickly, we had to support each other's recommendations wholeheartedly. A couple of days later, after work, I sat in a booth at Soirée meeting Simon, who was not only cool but had what I believe a previous generation would refer to as 'matinee idol good looks'. His handshake was so firm and confident I immediately felt inadequate and a sorry excuse for masculinity.

"I've heard great things about you, Alex. Julian thinks you are a marketing genius."

I stammered an incoherent reply and shrugged my shoulders in an attempt at modesty that looked more like a muscle spasm.

"Julian says you're the greatest accountant since..." My voice trailed off. You try to think of a famous accountant on the spot; it's not easy. I changed tack and thought I should at least ask some vaguely professional questions.

"So, where did you qualify?"

Julian and Simon exchanged a furtive glance, which I think, in retrospect, I mistook for irritation that I should have done my homework properly.

Julian answered for Simon in a way that suggested I had caused offence. "Simon has been finance director to many different businesses, including several who have had very healthy exits. He's very good at creating individual financial structures for different businesses."

"Guilty as charged," Simon added, with a humility that seemed a fraction insincere.

"What makes you think this is a good opportunity for you?"

"If Julian thinks this is huge, I'm in. We're always of one mind in anything we do. I have worked and raised money for many different digital businesses over the last five years. I am what you need, Alex. Trust me, I'm the man for this."

For the next fifteen minutes, he reeled off a series of obscure businesses and I was bombarded with acronyms and arrogant jargon. I knew what each term meant, but I couldn't extricate their context from a series of statements about companies I knew nothing about. He was basically asserting success in everything he had ever done.

He sat back and folded his arms and was momentarily distracted by a very pretty waitress refilling our glasses. I felt that the interview was over. As an interview, it was pretty one-sided and lacked the traditional core ingredient – the requirement to answer questions.

As suave as he was, I didn't know what to think. We had a pleasant conversation thereafter. Unlike us, he was most definitely single, and his conspiratorial conversation suggested he was of the opinion that the best approach to relationships was to have several running concurrently. He was unashamedly uninterested in our proposition. We could have told him that we were creating a business to get rid of nuclear waste by building schools on highly contaminated areas, and he would have told us he was in. He and Julian wanted to work together. There was no debate to be had.

Julian rang me first thing the next morning with puppyish enthusiasm. "How impressive is Simon?' he began.

"Well, if I was ten years younger and a woman, I'd be drooling."

"He can start in a week. He wants your input so he can begin validating our forecasts and projections."

"Are we going to see someone else? This is quite an important role, after all."

There was an uncomfortable silence.

"Alex, you're going to need a little more faith in my choices, if we're going to make this successful."

Slightly taken aback by his aloofness, I decided that this was a moment for unity and mutual faith.

"OK. Of course I trust your judgement. Tell him he's in. It'll be great to have the financial rigour in place. He can choose his own abacus or slide rule. Whatever he wants."

Business books, which I really can't abide, would suggest that 'your instinct is your most potent weapon'. However, when you have momentum and you are in a hurry, sometimes it is easier to ignore it. In Simon's case, I had no idea if he could even switch on a calculator.

* * *

When it came to the CTO, I was much more certain who I wanted to work with from the outset. There was no way to have confidence in the venture if I didn't know who was going to be my tech partner.

Dimitri Kharkachov was Ukrainian and a genius.

He had come to the UK as a twenty-year-old computer science graduate from the V. N. Karazin National University in Kharkiv, his home town. He was the son of an engineer who had built the telecommunications infrastructure in Ukraine, post the collapse of the Soviet Union. Dimitri was a science and maths genius. He entered university at sixteen, routinely coming top of any academic challenge that came his way. It seemed an inevitability that he would follow the guidance of his professors and complete a PhD, eventually spearheading important research projects to assert Ukraine's superiority over its neighbour and rival, Russia.

However, Dimitri's ambition had taken an unexpected turn, which his controlling parents could not have anticipated. Unbeknown to them, he was supplementing his meagre student existence by sitting in his dingy room moonlighting as a developer for some of the biggest digital brands in the world. As part of the virtual community of global expertise, he could work cheaply, remotely and quickly on any project.

He was truly remarkable. Attending the minimum number of classes, he effortlessly completed his work on time and to an impeccably high standard. His day was split into segments dedicated to the different strands of his commercial and academic work. He slept five and a half hours every night, which was the minimum amount of replenishment he needed, and always ate the same meal at the same time based on a plan he had created for himself to optimise nutrition and sustain consistent energy levels.

By the time he graduated, he had amassed a bank account with $60,000 and had worked on Airbnb's upgraded user review feature and Uber's driver app, as well as numerous projects for major brands. He had earned the nickname 'Dimitri Einstein' in this virtual world. Everyone wanted him on a project.

The day he graduated, he announced to his devastated parents (he was an only child and they lived for his accomplishments) that he had got a job in London, joining the team of a major digital build agency for whom he had worked remotely. They had recognised his astonishing ability and offered him a staggering salary for a twenty-year-old, moving him from drab suburban Kharkiv to a converted studio apartment in Shoreditch. He was that unique, and worth the disproportionate investment.

My good fortune was that, within two hours of him starting on his first day, I found myself in a meeting with him at the agency, where I was the managing partner. Dimitri's arrival was heralded like the signing of a junior striker from the Barcelona Reserves. We were all fascinated to meet this Mozart of the digital age.

Mozart isn't a bad analogy, as Dimitri was a prodigy with limited social ability. His English was perfect, and his soft accent sounded more American than anything else. But if your life has been spent behind a screen, eye contact can prove challenging. Dimitri soon earned a new nickname, 'Russian Rain Man', which he hated. Not the autistic reference, but the ignorance of his proud Ukrainian heritage.

Subconsciously, I realised that Dimitri could be an asset in my eventual escape plan. I therefore tried to befriend him and give him, as best I could, some tips on how to be, quite frankly, a little less weird. I explained that I wanted to help him integrate into the company better and we agreed to meet for a chat in a coffee shop every week, at the same time and table (he really didn't do flexibility).

He was very receptive to advice. Dimitri approached life's intricacies like a solvable mathematical equation. I found myself distilling social problems into made-up equations. If I told him that to have friends, you needed to make an effort, he would stare at me blankly. However, if I wrote down on a piece of paper the spurious notation *Friendship = Consideration + Empathy + Effort*, we were cooking on gas. As a consequence, he became totally committed to self-improvement. Soon, it was hard to hear his name mentioned, especially by women, without the comment: 'Oh Dimitri, he is so sweet.'

I grew to like him, and we became friends. He had a charming determination and his pursuit of a solution to any issue that confronted him was single-minded and absolute. He developed his own image, which some mistook for pretension but was basically a reflection of his adherence to routine and consistency. A white tee shirt, black jeans, white trainers. Summer or winter, and always pristine. Although still only twenty-three, he had a maturity that belied his stubble-free baby face, and a kinetic energy focused on solving the next technical challenge that came his way, as long as it was bigger than the last.

He was the first person I spoke to outside of my family about the opportunity. I texted him from a few extra days of paternity leave I'd decided to take, and asked if we could meet up. A confused response arrived: *Not normal meeting time. Why?* I had underestimated that recalibrating his routine was not always easy. I replied: *Big opportunity. Confidential.* Then, to arouse his inner coding ambition, I sent another one simply saying: *Technically huge challenge.*

Two days later, we sat in a discreet corner of our normal rendezvous location (not our regular table, engendering a bit more angst and fidgeting) and made brief small talk.

"Why have I not seen you for a while?" he asked.

"I'm taking some extra paternity leave. I've just had a daughter." Nope, he was none the wiser. Paternity leave and children were code he had not learnt to write or understand. Not an auspicious beginning for the concept I was about to pitch to him.

We caught up on his life. He had a new girlfriend from the office, which surprised me as he had never discussed anything intimate. I actually got more than I bargained for. He explained their dating routine, which had very little inherent romance and was operated with the rigour of a project plan. Drinks, dinner and sex were all slotted in with a fixed time allocation. I couldn't take any more time-based explanations of his relationship, so I kicked off the conversation.

"Dimitri, I want you to join me in a start-up that I think will make you rich and famous." It seemed, these days, that I couldn't chat without sounding like I was pitching or making grandiose statements.

"I'm not so interested in the money. But fame, I like. I want to be recognised as someone who can build anything. You know that, don't you?"

"I can promise you that you're the only person on this planet who can make this work." This language was getting out of hand. Was I ever going to be able to have a business conversation in which I was not hyperbolising the simplest comment?

"Tell me, Alex. Tell me how."

I knew Dimitri was going to be a part of this before I started to explain my thinking. He was as vain as any feckless artist or creative visionary. It wasn't conceit or self-belief but the competitive need to be better than anyone else. I therefore explained the idea in terms of global reach and scalability. Unsurprisingly, he had no interest in the proposition as he couldn't have cared less about a business based on assuaging parental guilt. He cared about functionality and distilled the challenges into three questions:

How could we create an experience that turned a need into a solution, and how would we create enough solutions?

How did we roll out globally?

And, most importantly, when could he start?

I stuttered vague answers to the first two questions but had a much more definitive response for the last one. We could hand in our resignations together. We'd have to be careful that it didn't look like I had poached him directly because I was sure I had a non-solicitation clause in my contract, but I was happy to stretch the truth if required to explain.

It was interesting that he asked so little about funding, revenue modelling and his ownership of this venture. His ambition was born out of his superior intelligence. It was propelled by a need to be the cleverest technician who could create something amazing from scratch. He either trusted me implicitly or did not have the emotional sophistication to worry about sacrificing everything to the whim of someone else's business idea.

We talked for three hours, until I got an angry text from Sarah yanking me back to the world of practical rather than virtual parenting. In that time, Dimitri had already started to shape a plan on how he was going to build my idea. Using his iPhone calculator and a scrap of paper, he mapped out the build time required and the structure of a team needed to help him along the way.

Dimitri was extremely animated by the time I got up to go and was scrawling code – indifferent, if not oblivious, to my departure. Sensing the momentous possibility of our future professional union, I quoted Humphrey Bogart, with an unconvincing attempt at an American accent.

"*Louis, I think this is the beginning of a beautiful friendship.*"

Without blinking or averting his gaze from his crazed working, he simply replied, "Who is Louis?"

"It's from *Casablanca*," I explained.

"Pointless conversation. I have never been there."

* * *

I needed someone to bang heads together and keep us all in check. As I spent more time with Julian, I realised that he was focused on doing the deal, rather than the softer values of people or company culture. I had a solution.

Alice Evans was the most ruthlessly organised person I had ever met. She had run major digital transformation projects (a bit of industry jargon for creating transactional websites and apps to help businesses operate differently) for nearly fifteen years. Her reputation was formidable, as she matched her efficiency with a determination that was rather scary.

Alice was riddled with integrity. She would always do the right thing even if it wasn't the most convenient option. She had a proper moral code. I couldn't even remember the code to my gym locker.

The adherence to good conduct and appropriateness came from her religious background. Her father was a Presbyterian minister in a small village, and she had been a bookish child who was obedient, courteous and deeply unhappy. In her teens, she grappled with her sexuality and realised, to quote the popular expression, that she was the 'only gay in the village'. She thus fled to study in London, settling into an urban life free from the judgement of a blinkered rural community. But she had absorbed the values of decency, hard work and spiritual courage that her father quietly promulgated from his tiny pulpit. This proved a formidable combination in the tech world she entered post-university. She had a mantra, which she referred to as the Eleventh Commandment for the digital age: 'Thou shalt not cut corners.'

Alice met her partner and future wife, Caroline, at university and they were the model of domestic calm. They had two small sons, and both worked hard in their respective careers (Caroline was a teacher). Alice was just a very nice person, with whom I worked for a number of years in the early part of my career and stayed close to thereafter. We helped each other with advice and guidance. She once told me that she wanted to have choices in her life so that she could do some good with her expertise. She proved you could do business ethically and also ensure that you managed your career to protect your own interests. We were, of course, going to put a strain on these values as we grew more successful.

We initially met to run through the idea and she got very excited, loving the concept of doing something positive for parents. She was an articulate advocate for non-traditional families. She didn't mention money, but I knew she would be mulling the possibility of taking a risk to reap a reward.

The chemistry the following day with Julian was not great. He had met Dimitri a few days previously and was already in love, never having met someone so completely controlled but also unshakeably convinced of his greatness. He told me that I had to handcuff myself to Dimitri and keep him happy with whatever it took: vodka, caviar, fast cars, girlfriends, boyfriends, obedient puppies or a new set of golf clubs.

The meeting with Alice was different. This was the person I told him we needed; however, it seemed far too pedestrian to warrant his engagement. He was courteous, but distracted by the constant ping of email traffic on his phone. There had been a slightly awkward moment when Alice asked him to explain his vision for PrimaParentand he had talked about investment, revenue and exit. He didn't acknowledge the mission or vision for making parenting better or children happier, which Alice had articulated in a speculative corporate manifesto she had drafted and brought to the meeting for discussion.

The conversation descended into Alice passionately explaining how she managed complex projects and difficult people, while Julian nodded sagely, his mind clearly focused elsewhere, fooling no one that he was actually absorbing anything. They both rang me after the meeting.

"Look, mate, if you think we need someone like her, I trust you. Just don't make me have to listen to her lecture me on why I can't fire someone because I don't like their trainers. I don't want us to become the Salvation Army of start-ups."

I reassured him and was quietly relieved that we were not going to argue. I knew that Alice could calmly organise a global evacuation to Mars, unfazed by complexity or scale. Moreover, she could do everything I couldn't, which was rather a lot. When we spoke, she was still unconvinced, latching on to the public-school urbanity that Julian exuded as a sign of 'casual amorality'. She was curious about how well I knew him.

In a slight rewriting of historical truth, I told her we had known each other socially for years and had actually worked on a project together for a shared client. I was slightly astounded how simple it was to invent such a porky at a moment of crisis. Indeed, I noted this would be a useful skill in times of stress moving forward. If I'd told her we met at a sandpit in a park a couple of months previously, she would have hung up. My well-intentioned veracity-stretching did the trick. I convinced her that we would be working closely together, and Julian's role, securing our commercial viability, would be separate from her crucial task of doing everything needed to make us function. I shamelessly pandered to her idealism.

"You'll make a difference to families' lives. And you can make a difference to your family's life at the same time."

"You are frighteningly slick, Alex. Have you already sold your soul to the devil?"

"Alice, shame on you. I'm a nice Jewish boy. We don't go in for that sort of thing."

She rang me the next day to tell me that she was in. She had discussed it long into the night with Caroline and they were prepared to remortgage their house and for Caroline to do an extra day of teaching if necessary.

"This is real, Alex, isn't it?"

"It is now," I replied, slightly nervously. We now had a grown-up on the team.

* * *

And what about Julian?

You have a sense of the tensions in my upbringing: a successful grandpa who made me want to build a business, tempered by academic non-materialistic parents who made me feel guilty for such ignoble aspirations. Emotionally, I am also a bit of an open book. If you ask me how I am, be prepared for a lengthy response.

Julian was much more guarded about what drove him, and while his desire for us to prosper was incontestable, he was unwilling to disclose his feelings. During our lengthy planning conversations, I would badger him to give me some context and colour about his life and occasionally he would assuage my inquisitiveness with a few details about his upbringing. In time, I managed to extricate an explanatory narrative.

He was the younger of two children and his older sister was the recipient of his father's intense love and affection. Stella was showered with gifts when times were good – a pony, a tree house and a beautiful room. She was an idealised version of her mother, a quiet submissive woman subjected to the philandering and financially frivolous behaviour of an indifferent husband. You don't have to be Freud to work your way round this one. Julian was his mother's relief in an unhappy house. She resented her husband's devotion to his daughter and his indifference to his son. Nothing Julian could do was enough for him.

He was shipped off to boarding school at seven while his sister was allowed to stay at home. His father was distant and critical and Julian had to be the best at every endeavour to get noticed. As it happens, he became a county-level tennis player of great promise. However, his father's aloofness created an unquenchable frustration and a temper that he couldn't control, and in the competitive fray of a match, it would overcome him at inopportune times. With a glint of satisfaction, Julian recalled how he was banned from competing for a while when, mired in a black fog, he went to the umpire's chair, called him a very nasty name and then proved how good at volleying he was by hitting a deliberate full-blooded shot into the unlucky man's testicles.

I have pieced this portrait together from various anecdotes, but I think it's accurate. Julian had several mantras that would emerge during different conversations, revealing his innate competitiveness and belief in self-reliance. His favourite was: 'Remember chaps, second place is first loser.' I thought it was impressive until Sarah told me one day it was what her primary school PE teacher used to say to them before a netball match. He was also very fond of reminding me to 'trust no one and you won't be disappointed'. There was a grittiness when dealing with Julian. He was charming until he didn't want to be. His demeanour would suddenly change to suggest he was in no mood for discussion or opinion-sharing.

Julian was impressively bright, and I was seduced by his professional allure. Like us all, however, he emerged as a complex intersection of behaviours and experiences. His drive was inspirational but his motivation more ambiguous. Not something you can always find out when you meet on a park bench.

4. The Idea

My head hurt.

All I could do was think, all day and every day, about my nascent business. I imagined its progress and visualised its success. I jotted ideas down wherever I was and irrespective of what I was doing. When I spent time with friends and family, my sentences were rarely completed as my flibbertigibbet mind moved on to the next thought. I was a complete pain to be around.

I was obsessed with getting all the detail right. Julian and I had assembled a team, but we had to have a credible story to tell and the investment opportunity had to be rooted in its relevance to consumers. Not only that, we needed spreadsheets, a logo, a tagline and some beautifully designed documents to make us look really professional.

Online marketplaces can quickly create unprecedented demand. There are some basic factors that engender success or create unmitigated failure. First of all, if you are thinking of starting something yourself, you need to ask how your market will grow. Liquidity is the term used to describe the effective viability of any prospective exchange: will there be a growing supply of customers actively searching your site? In turn, will there be a sufficiency of sellers to meet all of their needs and ensure they come back, tell their friends and evangelise your brilliance?

Once I have visited your site, has the experience been good enough to make me want to come back? Did I find what I was looking for? How was the customer service? Was the experience easy and convenient? Did you take my money without any effort? Has the enormous inflatable giraffe I ordered been delivered on time and without a hole in its neck? Will I come back again?

Finally, there is a basic economic consideration of how the market-place is going to make money based on the transactions it facilitates. Are you going to sell high-value items infrequently or low-value items regularly? Nirvana is selling something hugely expensive every week, for example an online cocaine store (*clickandsniff.com*).

Of course, I was not thinking about the huge margins of a drug business but better parenting for all. The business model for the transactional exchange was going to be based on a number of criteria. A proposed marketplace revenue of 4 per cent on every transaction would be applied. Further revenues would come from what are called seller services, things like promoted listings or processing payments on behalf of the seller. Any third-party processor would also be charged. As we grew and drove more traffic to the site, we could start to sell advertising and inventory too. We also needed to create a sense of perceived value that a subscription would necessitate. This relied on the basic principle of a subscription – keep it low and make it monthly and no one will remember to cancel if dissatisfied. We were banking (literally) on some healthy levels of inertia.

The next question was even more important. What were we going to sell and how were we going to ensure that we had enough of a breadth of products to make us an everyday indispensable service? My thinking was based on the key milestones in parenting.

Birthdays are, of course, crucial. Parties, presents and experiences. A piece of cake in a napkin, a sorry balloon and a book token just won't do these days. Little Tommy's seventh birthday requires the precision planning of a royal wedding or the election of the next pope. Distinct presents that are limited edition, celebratory bespoke decorations, cakes that are multilayered and themed, personalised invitations, elaborate bunting, party bags, thank-you cards, vats of

Calpol to ensure they stay healthy throughout the day, single malt and Pinot Grigio for Mum and Dad. The possibilities are endless.

It's not just birthdays that need innovation and invention – other special occasions do too: bar mitzvahs and confirmations, exam success, sporting achievements, the arrival of the tooth fairy and the departure of your appendix or adenoids. Anything that requires a bit of parental pampering. But that is just the start.

Interminable school holidays? Weeks and weeks of empty diary space to fill. Playdates to orchestrate, places to visit, activities to invent from thin air. A guaranteed place in parent heaven if you manage to help them learn to origami the Leaning Tower of Pisa and the next day to juggle fire or unicycle. What if they are incentivised to sew their own costumes and put on a production of *The Merry Wives of Windsor* in your front room? How about you create a bespoke treasure hunt that keeps them entertained as they search out clues on your local high street based on the Victorian sewer system?

Then there are designer clothes that are environmentally friendly or tee shirts you can eat. There are online violin lessons for beginners so that you can decide if it is worth investing in their future virtuosity. Tap-dancing tuition and tango training for the romantic ten-year-old. What about more unusual exercise – yoga for tots, Pilates for prepubescents and circuit training for the badly co-ordinated? Bespoke stationery for messy left-handers, calculators for the short-sighted and puffy-fingered, wipe-off-the-floor oil paints, modelling clay you can microwave? You get the idea. Anyone who could promote a facet of modern parenting was a potential seller.

The final category was a publishing idea of Julian's. He had worked on licensing deals with a number of publishing houses over the years and knew the sector well. He wanted us not simply to be able to provide products and services but to be an entertainment hub, and he had lots of interesting ideas. We could publish new authors' works, create exclusive deals on audio books for established authors, and have a classics section where we opportunistically grabbed interesting (but possibly overlooked) works that had lapsed out of copyright. More ambitiously, we could work with production companies and create our own programming.

We wrote a six-year business plan with full revenue and cost projections and somehow, due to optimistic maths and prodigious chutzpah, arrived at a valuation by then of over £100m. We factored in rolling out the business globally and identified the first ten markets from which we would fan out our all-conquering empire. Julian and Simon were adamant that we create a hockey stick forecast, a term used for visually representing a miraculous increase in profitability after an initial flat period, while I favoured something more gently shaped. Julian attacked my conservatism late one evening when we were nearing the plan's completion.

"Alex, am I marrying a little worrier, or do you sometimes cross the road without looking for the fun of it?"

"I don't know what you're talking about. I am totally reckless in everything I do."

"Seriously, mate, you have to realise that if you project a scintilla of doubt or nervousness, any prospective backer will run for the hills."

He was right that I would have to develop a poker face going forward. I didn't doubt my ability to embellish when necessary, even when asking someone for money, but Julian's brazenness was chilling. The truth was clearly a distraction when it came to asking people for lots of money.

"I suppose I just need to keep some grounding in reality," I conceded.

Julian gave me a look of withering condescension. "As my father used to say before they locked him up, 'Don't burden your ambition with a conscience.'"

"Positively Buddhist in its sentiment," I quipped, and we carried on until the wee hours, steepening the angle of our revenue fantasies.

* * *

The business plan was a thing of beauty. Quite literally. It was art-directed by a designer friend who took my brief of 'make it look good to hide the content' a little *too* literally. Hand-drawn graphics, elegantly illustrated tables of figures – the whole thing conferred a stature that we were going to require if we wanted to be taken seriously.

Julian and I had debated what we needed the plan to say to get us the requisite funding. We had taken the collective decision that in order to grow at speed, we were going to have to get in quite a lot of money very quickly. There was very little time to attract lots of sellers and customers to the site concurrently, and we would not be able to do this with an operation that was made up of just a few of us. Rapid growth at all costs was going to be our corporate mantra.

Our sums went as follows. We calculated an initial value of £9m for the company. We would keep about 30 per cent each. We would keep around 10 per cent for junior partners (to date, Simon, Dimitri and Alice) and we would split the remaining 30 per cent between, ideally, two or three backers who would fund our first eighteen months or so until some revenue arrived. The more money we borrowed over time, the more, of course, we would have to dilute our own stake.

We were going to be frugal in our set-up and ascetic in behaviour. None of us would draw a salary of any sort for six months, then the junior partners would receive a modest allowance to help them pay their bus fare and buy sliced white bread and margarine for tea. Julian and I would remain salary-free for a year and then receive a very basic wage. Money was going to be tight at home.

Julian had done incredibly well to find a minimal-rent loft in Clerkenwell, left empty when a gaming app company had mysteriously disappeared as HMRC were threatening to break down the doors. He'd gone to school with the landlord and always bought the guy a Bakewell tart at the tuck shop, so was therefore owed a massive favour. We were launching in a 3,000-square-foot industrial-chic space wrapped in stainless steel and chrome, with its own goods lift and a professional Gaggia coffee machine kindly left to us by the previous tenants, unable to dismantle it as they fled to avoid debtors' prison. The only other thing we had to pay for was water and electricity, and I had every intention of only allowing infrequent toilet flushes. Plus, the twilight glare of a laptop meant we'd not have to switch the lights on.

The final thing we needed was a logo and a strapline. You can create spreadsheets and anticipate imaginary growth forever, but a business that has the ambition to change global behaviour needs to look and sound cool. This was the most complicated part of our initial planning phase because Julian and I could not agree about anything. I took responsibility for its creation, begging favours from a range of former colleagues. I whittled the logos down to a choice of six very different designs. Julian turned out to be worse than any client I had ever had in demonstrating strong prejudice aligned to vague feedback.

"They just don't make my heart skip a beat," he opined as I spread the papers before him in his living room.

"You know, a good logo doesn't need a defibrillator," I retorted. It sounded an impressive comeback at the time, but on reflection it was a bit meaningless and Julian had looked flummoxed.

"I'm sorry, Alex, but they're all mundane. They'll make us as famous as Peter Higginbottom."

"Who's Peter Higginbottom?"

"My point entirely. He's my next-door neighbour."

"I think you're totally wrong. I think one of them nails it and will work very well indeed. It'll look great online. It'll look great on tee shirts."

Julian leaned forward and challenged me to elaborate.

"Go on then, punk. Which one of these designs do you think is worthy of my ambition for this business?"

I perhaps should have stopped at that point to consider what he'd just said. *His* ambition? I was so galvanised to resolve the logo issue that adrenaline precluded me from processing this rather arrogant self-importance. It was true that as we worked later and harder to get the plan completed, I missed quite a few little comments that later struck me as unnecessarily barbed. That night I was resolved simply to get him to agree an identity that would allow us to develop a look for the design of the business.

"This is the one and the only one that will do." I held the design several inches from his face in my attempt to prevent him disagreeing.

"I'll go with it because you seem so insistent. But if it backfires and affects the business, I will hold you responsible and probably sue."

I initially thought that this statement was just more banter. But Julian got up very quickly and grabbed our coffee mugs and marched towards the kitchen, leaving me unable to process his mood and deflated at having agreed the right identity for the business but without any pleasure.

"Goodnight, Alex, I'll see you tomorrow," he shouted flatly from the kitchen. The meeting was over, and I saw myself out.

The logo we selected will, of course, be familiar to you. The 'P' of 'Prima' is also used to form the word 'Parent' below. The simple visual representation of parenting is also multicoloured to remind you how warm and friendly we are. Rather clever, and it even won a design award back in 2013.

* * *

The final thing we needed was the strapline, which would encapsulate our aspiration for the business and its benefits ford its loyal global customers. In addition, this line needed to work in other languages – after all, you can't conquer the world if they laugh at your syntax.

We brainstormed this one with the wider team. Julian and I wanted to democratise the process, so everyone was allowed to participate. We gathered one lunchtime at a large table hidden at the back of a Soho coffee shop. It was the first time Simon, Alice and Dimitri had met. We all shouted out ideas, except Dimitri, who sat writing code in the corner. After twenty minutes, he put some enormous headphones on to drown out this marketing piffle. The four of us shouted out trite phrases.

"Happy children deserve better parents."

"Be a better parent every day."

"Parenting made easy."

It was all superficial, selling and soulless. By this stage, I was pacing with a marker pen in my hand, pretending I was going to eliminate child poverty. After forty-five minutes, we had scrawled some nonsense on a flip chart pad but the energy in the room was dissipating and my perkiness was starting to irritate everyone. In a throwaway comment, I mentioned that my obsession with the business was beginning to scare Sarah. She had demanded of me that 'however hard I was going to work, not to forget that it was always family first'.

It was Alice who leapt to her feet.

"Oh, that's it. So bloody obvious."

"What is?" I asked.

"Sarah's cracked it," she continued in a voice that was now shouting. *"Family First.* It says what we do. Prima means First. We help people put their families ahead of anything else in the world.

And it says something about us as an organisation. We should work hard, but Sarah is spot on. We must not lose sight of who we really are and what matters in our personal lives. It's brilliant."

Julian and Simon's faces betrayed their bemusement. They looked as if they were stuck on a yoga retreat with an overly spiritual shaman. It was just not the way they thought. I felt differently.

"You are so right, Alice. *Family First*. It's going to make us famous, and I bet it works in Swedish too." I saw exciting possibilities ahead.

"Are we going to get some food, I am starving," Dimitri chimed in, taking off his headphones and sensing the end of the meeting.

The boring bit was over. It was time to raise some money.

5. Family Matters

Julian and I resigned from our jobs with alacrity. I think I did everyone a bit of a favour, as the agency was struggling – quite frankly, my salary was a welcome saving, and we agreed that I could go immediately. I thought of filling my rucksack with staplers and photocopier toner, but in the end I slipped out quietly one Friday with a few Amazon vouchers, a hastily purchased card from the corner shop and the hope I'd never work for someone else again. Julian, on the other hand, invited me to his grand leaving drinks, which all the partners attended as if bidding a regretful farewell to their own offspring. He was infuriatingly popular.

I decided it was time to introduce each other to our respective families. Sarah was increasingly fascinated by the mysterious individual who had driven me from the marital bed to late-night business planning sessions. She wasn't suspicious but wanted reassurance that this new sense of mission permeating my every utterance was shared with someone worthwhile.

"After all," she told me during one midnight feed when I returned home, "if I'm going to lose you to Julian, I want to know that he won't dump you when a more attractive entrepreneur comes along."

We hastily arranged a dinner a few days later. I suggested they come to our house for a takeaway. Initially, Julian seemed reluctant and a bit uncertain why it was necessary. I knew his wife, Catherine, was a management consultant and, like Sarah, on maternity leave, but she rarely came up in conversation. I was always quoting Sarah's thoughts as if she was a silent partner in the venture. Catherine, on the other hand, was most decidedly an irrelevance to any of our plans. After cajoling Julian with the promise of my best wine and as many Pringles as he could eat, he relented and sent a quick text to Catherine confirming a date and time. He remained overtly ambivalent to the evening and would probably have preferred a trip to the local crematorium over a night out with his wife.

Sarah had ignored the suggestion of a takeaway and prepared a lovely dinner during snatched respite when Emily was sleeping. When they arrived, Julian was initially at his most engaging and began a conversation with her, nodding enthusiastically as if they were on a blind date. I talked to Catherine, who was polite but uneffusive. I stared at my shoes a fair bit to avoid the awkward silences that seemed to be the result of my attempts at small talk. She became more energised when I enquired about her professional life. She was a partner at a small tech consultancy and couldn't wait to be back at work, unrepentant for her disdain for her current status.

"You're meant to love being at home with children. I have three screaming brats – four if you include Julian." She smiled at her joke and gulped half of her second glass of Merlot without pausing. If she was still breastfeeding, she would have a comatose child that night.

"So, what do you think of our idea?" I asked. She would have some very interesting thoughts on the subject, given the nature of the advisory work she did every day for her digitally based clients. I was actually anxious to receive her validation.

"I'm afraid I don't really know too much about it." She looked rather sheepish, as if realising how absurd that sounded.

"Don't joke," I continued, "I'm sure you know more about what we need to do than any of us. I'd really welcome some advice."

"That's very kind of you, Alex, to have such belief in me. But Julian is less convinced. He's said it's something to do with parenting, but that's about it. After recovering from the shock of Julian having an interest in anything to do with children, I haven't really pushed him on it."

"Why not?" I asked, fearful that their marital health was not what I wanted to hear about. Catherine responded angrily.

"Because I'm afraid you don't know my husband that well. You've probably been ensnared by his effortless charm and wit. Happens to us all. I'm afraid, Alex, my husband has the ethics of a serial killer. You've probably heard the whole routine about his father in prison, as if this has given him a focus and justification for success. Julian is just a bloke on the make who has a tremendous sense of entitlement. He wants money and he wants recognition. Doesn't care about anyone and would quite literally decapitate anyone who stands in the way. You'll be wondering why we're still together?"

Too right I was. I was also wondering how much more unpleasant the evening could become and if I was about to enter into a business marriage that would end up loveless and bitter because I had fallen for a sociopath. The awkwardness was punctured by Sarah arriving from the kitchen, where she had been chatting with Julian, and announcing it was time to eat. I mumbled something to Catherine about being sorry. I may have also mentioned that Sarah's pesto sauce was going to be delicious. I was not managing to hide my embarrassment convincingly.

We adjourned to the dining room. Sarah, sensing the tension between our guests, launched into conversation with Catherine, while Julian and I talked about our forthcoming pitches for money. They could have been strangers, so little did they interact. I also noticed with some trepidation that I was pouring wine with an unfamiliar frequency. A couple of glasses and I'm groggy and liable to fall asleep, even when standing. Julian and Catherine drank with swagger and gusto, emptying glass after glass as I struggled to open another bottle with the complicated sommelier's corkscrew I'd been given for my wedding.

"I'm going to have to switch to screw tops – it'll be so much quicker," I whispered to Sarah as we cleared the plates.

"They hate each other," Sarah replied with alarm. "She's been telling me – when she thinks he's not listening – that he is ruthless. Do you know what you're doing?"

I was, of course, very concerned, but couldn't let on to Sarah. You don't alienate your number-one supporter. "Sarah, his marriage is not relevant to our business. It's unfortunate, but not really going to have an impact."

"Oh Alex, you don't believe this, do you? The way he treats his wife is going to be the way he treats his company. Smell the coffee, please."

Trying to avoid the issue deftly, I took out a packet of coffee beans from the cupboard and inhaled theatrically. "Smells delicious."

Sarah rolled her eyes with familiar disappointment and walked towards the table to confront the glacial silence that had descended between husband and wife. She was ever the elegant host who knew how to behave, irrespective of the situation. "Who wants lemon tart?"

Julian, slurring, swaying and long past coherence, held out his plate. Catherine seemed tearful. I counted the minutes until I could call them a cab.

* * *

My first pitch was not to an investor, but to my family a couple of days later, round the Friday-night dinner table at my parents' house.

Throughout the world, Jewry is bound together by many traditions, directives and observances, but the most common shared practice is the family gathering around a Sabbath table each week. Candles are lit and blessings are uttered briefly over bread and wine, followed by dinner. For the Lazarus family, it was often a time for contemplation, personal updates, and political disagreement as my father would hold court on the latest academic theory and I would try to argue, primarily just to annoy him.

When we met that Friday, my sister was present, as well as an elderly uncle of my father's. Judith had fulfilled our mother's prediction of future success and was the chief operating officer of an influential humanitarian agency, Better Futures, that ran programmes for displaced children in areas of conflict across the globe. She was thirty-five and responsible for overseeing an organisation of one hundred and fifty people, a budget of tens of millions, demanding donors, and a high-profile board all with egos in need of constant validation. She struggled to relax or settle down, travelled extensively and openly professed that as long as children were suffering as a result of war anywhere in the world, her job remained unfinished. Whenever she'd ask about my work, I'd sheepishly admit that I had just built a very cool game for the Frosties website, which made me look rather callow, with little prospect of admission into heaven any time soon.

That night, I wanted to tell them my plans. I had been so absent over recent months that I knew they suspected something awry. As we started to eat, I nervously clinked my glass and declared I had an announcement. There was immediate silence and I saw a look flit across my mother's face as she glanced at Sarah, wondering if I had got her pregnant again so soon after Emily's arrival. Sarah guessed what my mother was thinking and looked at her stomach while vigorously shaking her head.

"I've left my job," I proclaimed, "and am setting up a new business that's going to make me very rich and successful."

Silence. As you will have realised by now, my tendency to speak in pronouncements, not sentences, was rather grating. It required people to have to focus on what I was saying as if it was crucial information, when actually it was superficial validation I was seeking.

"What's so important about being rich and successful?" my mother asked after a while. "Why not simply say 'I am going to do something worthwhile'?" She glanced at my sister and added for good measure, "Like Judith."

I ignored this familiar refrain and started to tell the story from the point at which the idea germinated in my mind after meeting Julian. I outlined how the site would work, how much money we would need to raise and what it would be worth in five years.

My father was midway through writing his latest book, a study of US capitalist tycoons with a working title of *Building the American Dream – From Vanderbilt to Jobs: A Study of Economic Tyranny*. He was particularly attuned to the evils of unnecessary wealth creation. When I finished my five-minute precis of the business plan, he simply stared at me and said: "Why, Alex? Why?"

"Why what?" I challenged.

"Why does your ego need to build its own legacy based on the creation of more artificial demand?"

"Dad, I'm not in one of your seminars. How about speaking to me as your son, not a PhD student."

For a second, my father seemed tempted to expound his theory on the capitalist axis of tech evil. He saw economic imperialism in any digital organisation's global success. Instead, a look of weary resignation came across his jowly face and he muttered into his plate, as if addressing his lamb chop, "I'm afraid I don't fully understand your ambition. I think there is so much more interesting work you could do."

I seethed with a combination of righteous indignation and an eight-year-old child's upset when told off by a parent. Great Uncle Norman, Zayde's youngest brother and business partner, was ninety-two and slightly deaf, but with undiminished mental acuity.

Sensing the escalation of tension, he looked at me kindly and said, "Your grandfather would have been very proud and would probably have invested in your venture, although you'd never be able to afford the terms." My sister, ever the diplomat, walked round the table and gave me an enormous hug.

"You go for it, Alex. I'll be furious if you don't succeed. I'm expecting a few million from your charitable foundation when you have your IPO."

The mood gradually lightened, as I was able to talk more about the plan for the business. My father asked forensic questions about its model. He understood the practicalities of digital growth far more than his negative stance on economic oligarchs would have suggested. I loved him dearly, but his disdain for commercial achievement and wealth annoyed me intensely. He lived a prosperous life, despite his principles – a combination of inherited wealth from my entrepreneurial grandfather and a media career that allowed him to rail against the system that was paying him so well. My mother was more empathetic and understanding. It's just that I was not quite as noble and praiseworthy as Judith or Sarah. By dessert, we were all calmer, and I was being teased by the table for my constant need to make everything sound like I'm trying to sell something.

"Go on, Alex," Judith said, "why don't you pitch another idea. It's been at least ten minutes."

"Only if you can guarantee that it exploits some workers," added my father, enjoying himself now. I yawned theatrically.

"Quick, someone call a surgeon. Saint Judith and Karl Marx have split my sides."

My mother grew tired of our caustic jousting and looked at me earnestly. "What is your new partner – Julian – like?"

Sarah glanced furtively at me, which my hyper-perceptive mother picked up on immediately. "What is he not telling us, Sarah?"

"It's all right," I said. "You know they respect your opinion more than mine."

'Well," she faltered, "I am so excited for Alex. It's just I think he's gone into business with someone who can't be trusted."

* * *

When you're focused on something, you push everything extraneous to the back of your mind. You think about what you crave, and it becomes easier to ignore things that may get in the way. You may wonder at this point why I was so driven that I chose not to confront some of Julian's initial bad manners. Simply put, I had developed a myopic obsession with my future, and I could not jeopardise the venture, having waited so long to find an outlet for the drive for success instilled in me by my grandfather's interminable lectures on how to count stock.

Ambition was an ephemeral desire that I did not know how to regulate. Being better, striving for something else, learning something new – these had all been subconscious impetuses for my actions since I was a student. As a history undergraduate, I had even written a worthy dissertation entitled 'Did the Ancient Greeks Invent Ambition?' I won't paraphrase my academic brilliance, except to leave you with one interesting fact about Hellenic culture.

The Ancient Greeks struggled to find a word for ambition. In fact, despite the clear aspirations of Alexander the Great for world domination, the concept of personal growth was hard for them to define. Instead, scholars point out that the three Greek words that have been translated into the English word 'ambition' are *philotimia*, literally 'love of honour'; *eritheia*, 'rivalry' or 'strife'; and *philodoxia*, 'love of acclaim'. Bear that in mind. Ambition can be rooted in the desire for glory and praise, but it also has inbuilt conflict. While classical civilisation viewed this quest as political rather than commercial, ask yourself why people chase a unicorn. It is not just the money. We all want immortality.

6. Money Please

We wanted money.

By November 2012, we had two weeks of continuous meetings impressively arranged by Julian. He really did know a lot of connected people: VCs, tech funds, investors, as well as wealthy individuals who were happy to speculate their vast fortunes on enthusiastic opportunists with a genius idea. We just needed to sound compelling.

We rehearsed our presentations and decided it would be me, Julian and Dimitri who attended the meetings. I would present the vision, brand and plan for growth. Julian would ask for money. Dimitri would sit enigmatically in the corner and answer any technical questions with disdain. It was pretty rudimentary, but at least it was a strategy.

We began with the venture capital firms looking to give seed investment to digital businesses. We were a bit agnostic about these opportunities. Yes, they had lots of experience in picking winning businesses, but it would come at the price of their involvement in our initial decision-making. We naively wanted to have independence in return for their hefty donation, promising of course that we'd send them a Christmas card and tell them how we were doing.

The first meeting was spectacularly unsuccessful. The demo site Dimitri had built did not open and could not be made to work. Sadly, it is not that impressive to ask for lots of money for a digital build if you come across as techno-plonkers. Dimitri hit the key of his MacBook with a ferocity that was bordering on abusive. A series of Ukrainian insults were hurled across the room and a fire burned in his eyes as he slammed the computer shut and shouted: "You have substandard Wi-Fi. Of course nothing will work."

Julian and I were by this time completely out of reassuring plat-itudes and suggested we move on, which received enthusiastic nods from eight bemused people in the room. Sadly, not Dimitri, who seemed affronted by the technological commitment of this tinpot firm that remarkably presided over a $750m tech fund.

"This is completely unsatisfactory. We must stop now," he yelled demonically, his eyeballs bulging as he projected spittle over an innocent nearby intern. Somehow, we managed to continue, but the magic had evaporated, and we gabbled through the rest of the presentation desperate for the fire alarm to go off suddenly so we could evacuate the room. When we concluded, the senior partner rose immediately and said that he had to go to lunch, even though it was 10.45 a.m. A scuffle almost broke out as the rest of the team fought their way to the door and freedom from us.

We spoke to Dimitri and tried to explain that investors buy people as much as they buy ideas and technology. It was therefore not a great idea to come across as psychotic in a meeting. He apolo-gised, but without much sincerity.

The next meetings went much better and generated real interest. We had become a really good double act by now. Most importantly, Dimitri was relegated to the bit part of computer operator. We allowed him to give a couple of truly unintelligible answers that would have bludgeoned even the most Scrooge-like investor into writing a cheque just to make him stop explaining how the algorithm worked. By the end of the first week we had a couple of very clear promises of invest-ment from firms who wanted us to commit to them immediately. However, something wasn't working for us and they did not feel like suitable partners to walk down the start-up aisle with.

We had one very amusing meeting with an elderly widow who was 210th in the *Sunday Times* Rich List thanks to her late husband's famous furniture empire ('Kingdom of Comfort'). She was eighty-one but dressed much younger and it was not a good look. Her advisor was a scruffily dressed grandson, Jed, who described himself as a tech savant and had diverted a small amount of the proceeds from leather sofas to create a fund, which he encouraged his grandmother to spend.

It was hard to be entirely serious in a quest for millions when the investor was being referred to as 'Nan' by her consigliere. She could not have been less interested in the idea and made it clear that 'my lovely boy Jed' made the decisions. Rather more alarmingly, she had succumbed to the rakish charm of Julian and her behaviour became increasingly coquettish. Whenever he said anything she laughed effusively, placing an arthritic hand on his knee and letting it linger a little longer each time.

As we got in the taxi afterwards, I told Julian, "I think we should take her money, Julian. I know I shouldn't objectify you, but really your looks are devastating and can save having to answer all those nasty technical questions."

Julian smiled with the assured knowledge that this was an occupational hazard for one so fair. "I feel cheapened and dirty. I thought working with you would be different."

Julian did get a text the next day that simply said: *Nan very impressed and would love to see you again ASAP to find out more.*

* * *

The real pitches were to come. On a chilly Sunday morning in November, we sat at our favourite table in Manuela's and Julian looked particularly pleased with himself.

"Great news. I've fixed us up a couple of meetings with some interesting backers who are very excited to meet us."

"Well, it's about time you did something useful," I quipped.

He looked momentarily irritated but carried on. "You and I are going to meet Lord Dobson of Cresswell in the House of Lords.

Following that, we're going to meet one of your boys, an Israeli entrepreneur, Moshe Shalon."

At that time, I had no idea that Julian had progressed to fixing up funding meetings – we hadn't even finished writing our plan. I was intrigued, if slightly caught off guard.

"I know I should know who Lord Dobson is, but I'm drawing an aristocratic blank. Is he famous?"

"His fame is irrelevant – it's his influence that's important. He's enormously wealthy and has bankrolled the Tories for thirty years. He's also my godfather."

"Excellent, he'll hopefully make us an offer we can't refuse. However, let me set you straight on something. Just because the other bloke is called Moshe doesn't mean we are related."

* * *

Lord Dobson of Cresswell, aka George Dobson from Stratford, was one of the country's richest property owners, who quietly exerted his will in order to control many aspects of Conservative rule. He was born in 1944 to a barrister father and a mother who was an only child and sole heir to the family's enormous portfolio of property. This became a reality for her a few years later, when her father was found dead from a heart attack at fifty-six in a bed that wasn't his (it allegedly belonged to a young aspiring actor called Gavin de Blois).

The property business ticked over, providing the family a yearly income that was more than generous. When George was twenty-two, he graduated from Balliol with a first in PPE, and the empire found its Napoleon driven to march in search of new conquests. George excelled in everything he did: a brilliant student, fine sportsman and aspiring politician. He was President of the Oxford Union in his first year, and at home smoking cigars with Tory grandees and cabinet ministers. As soon as he announced he was taking charge of the family property interests, he ousted the long-serving manager and started to plot a vast and ambitious expansion.

Over the next ten years, he built an enormous portfolio of interests, almost unnoticed. He owned shopping centres, Stalinist-looking flats sold to councils, luxury residences across the poshest parts of London, including much of Holland Park and Kensington, as well as office blocks in the City and West End. George's reputation was built on an aura of ruthlessness shrouded in secrecy.

He had married his Oxford sweetheart, Jennifer, shortly after graduating. They had three children and were together for thirty-five years. In 2005, he swapped her for Irina, a former ballerina from a small town outside St Petersburg; he had met her on the yacht of an oligarch with whom he was building a hotel in the Cotswolds. In 2009 he became a father again.

That was all I could find out about Lord Dobson. His business was a labyrinth of private companies, hard to connect. His political influence was legendary but also deliberately opaque. He first became known in 1979 when his donation paid for some of the famous advertising that brought Margaret Thatcher to power. Throughout her tenure, he appeared in a few photos, but always lurking in the shadows. However, the arrival of David Cameron saw him emerge from the murk to take on the role of 'strategic advisor' to the party leader. No one knew how this had happened.

Profiles started to appear peppered with descriptors like 'mysterious', 'charming' and 'ruthless', and his business was referred to as 'deliberately impenetrable'. The more well-known he became, the more PR consultants he employed to obscure the truth. He also developed a penchant for personal security and was famed for his increasing devotion to burly bodyguards to protect him from intrusion. He told *The Times* in 2010: 'If you marry a glamorous Russian, you can never be too careful.'

"He was at Oxford with my father," Julian explained over the remnants of our crushed avocado breakfasts. "When we were kids, we'd often holiday with the Dobsons. Lovely times on his boat on the Côte d'Azur or skiing in St Moritz."

"Did he not like caravanning then?"

"Alex, cover up that chip on your shoulder. It's unsightly."

"Well, what's he like then?"

Julian looked contemplative. He clearly had a genuine emotional connection with him. "Lovely godfather. Bloody hates kids, though."

"A bit ironic given we're pitching PrimaParent, don't you think?"

"Maybe. Maybe. But when Dad got done for his pathetic attempt at insider dealing, George was the only one to stand by him. Every month, without fail, he'd visit him in prison. And when he came out, he gave him a responsibility-free job with a generous allowance for nice lunches. We'll always be grateful that he helped mitigate our family's shame."

"I wonder what he'll make of me?"

Julian said nothing.

* * *

If you want an antithetical alternative to Lord Dobson then look no further than publicity-seeking Moshe Shalon. He loved attention and was disarmingly open in his opinions, which he shared most hours of the day on social media. His story is well known.

He was born on Kibbutz Degania Alef in 1974 to a family who had been there for three generations. The Israeli kibbutz movement was the backbone of the idealistic socialist state created in 1948. Communities were built on the basis of shared wealth and unquestioned egalitarianism. There were also pioneering agricultural experiments, producing fruit and vegetables where nothing had grown before. A kibbutznik was above all resilient to the elements and a potentially hostile environment, as well as fiercely protective of the community that he or she helped to create.

Moshe Shalon learnt fortitude, entrepreneurial innovation, bravery and determination from his kibbutz upbringing. Egalitarianism, however, was most definitely not for him. He had a decorated army career as a front-line paratrooper and then decided after four terms at university that he didn't need to be a mechanical engineer to start his own business. Rather, he would surround himself with technical expertise to grow a commercial enterprise with the same tenacity his grandparents had shown in creating fertile land from swamp, but with untold riches that he would not have to share.

Moshe launched SmickSmack in 1997 in the nascent days of the internet, when online shopping was still a distant, scarcely believable promise. He had met Avi Ram, a twenty-six-year-old computer programmer, in a rare class he had attended during his fleeting university career, where he had overheard the professor tell Avi that he'd never met a student like him and that he was destined for greatness. Those words galvanised Moshe to befriend the innocent and unworldly Avi Ram for purposes of future financial gain. He also thought it was hysterical that his surname was a measurement of data storage, which had to be God's way of saying 'use this chap for all he's worth'.

Under Moshe's rigid and ruthless control, Avi developed an evolutionary suite of data encryption software. These products were sold with unrelenting determination by a team of salespeople trained with the paratrooper-inspired adherence to duty that Moshe had learnt in the army. His genius was twofold. He understood technology trends and could shape products to meet them. The other aspect was his thirst for acquisition, quenched by an endless absorption of smaller businesses to ensure that the threat of competition was eliminated. When the dot-com crash rattled the industry in the early part of the noughties, Moshe had insulated his empire from collapse by concentrating on unaffected growth areas. He became crucial to the financial services industry and was also awarded contracts by the Israeli Ministry of Defence, about which very little was known.

Moshe Shalon's profile in *Forbes* magazine in 2006 estimated that he was worth $600m, which irked him because he felt that success was not real unless you earned the 'billionaire' moniker. Life was pretty good, especially when he married Ilana Hamdi, a former Miss Israel, swimsuit model and now an aspiring singer. He had supported her in the production of an album, *Kol Kushti*, which had enjoyed modest success in a few smaller European pop charts. A media commentator and well-known figure in Tel Aviv nightlife, Moshe was respected by the business community, and famous for having a cruel sense of humour and not being very kind to those he didn't respect.

I knew a little bit about Moshe Shalon before I met him and was aware that SmickSmack was one of Israel's most respected tech companies. His brutal reputation didn't scare me. I had run large digital transformation projects for entrepreneurial founders, who at best were mercurial in temperament but were often ranting despots. I was actually quite calm under pressure. A particularly unhinged client, furious at a delay in an app launch, had phoned me recently at home at 1 a.m. to shout incessantly at me for an hour. It included the rather memorable insult: 'You are a dimwit, so dim-witted you are too dim-witted to even win "Dimwit of the Year".' How much more challenging could Moshe Shalon be?

* * *

We visited Lord Dobson first.

It was a bitterly cold late-November day. The Houses of Parliament looked Gothically imposing against a slate-grey sky as we got out of a cab. I glanced at the crenelations and made a mental note that it was impressive I remembered the word 'crenelation' from lessons on Norman architecture at school. A gargoyle on one of the battlements looked down at me with contempt. It seemed to be saying: *You're never going to get funding for that idea, mate.*

We had left Dimitri behind, believing the austerity of our surroundings and the formality of our host may not be the perfect environment for him. Julian had reminded me to be smartly attired, so I'd had my Boss suit dry-cleaned and had polished my rather ancient black leather Italian shoes. I decided against a tie as I had not worn one for several years and felt it unnecessary. Julian, as you would expect, achieved sartorial one-upmanship that day. He took off his navy cashmere coat to reveal an impeccable bespoke three-piece suit that made me feel like a scarecrow. His tie was brightly emblazoned with a crest that suggested an elite club membership from which I was excluded. It wasn't quite the vibe of a digital maven, but he looked like he was born to rule over lesser mortals like me.

We were shown into the guest dining room and the maître d' whispered in my ear, "I am afraid, sir, you will need to wear a tie." Flushed with embarrassment, I selected one quickly from his station and started to tie it as quickly as I could. At that precise moment, I heard Julian greet George Dobson with enthusiasm. I turned to see a look of enormous disdain on our host's handsome face as he watched me fumble with the knot.

"It's a pleasure to meet you, sir," I stammered.

"Call me George, young man, and might I suggest you find out a little bit more about our dress code next time you visit." As a prelude to asking a very influential man for millions, it was inauspicious.

Julian came to my rescue quickly and deflected him with family gossip. They talked with warmth about Julian's father, who, despite his dodgy financial dealings, was clearly someone Lord Dobson adored. He told several anecdotes about their schooldays, which were neither funny nor legal, but I suppose they were different times and you could get away with keeping an air rifle in your bedroom if you were a boarder.

We ordered lunch and Julian and our host embarked on a vigorous debate about the clarets on offer in the House of Lords' cellar. I smiled nervously, worried that I would say something facile about the 2006 Pomerol he ordered that would make him hate me more. When my glass was filled, I thought of proffering that I felt the blackcurrant acidity beautifully offset the caramel and buttery top notes.

Fortunately, my silence allowed his indifference to abate and after the small talk stopped, he turned to me with a faint trace of a smile and said: "So, Alex, Julian tells me you have an ambitious plan for world domination, but you need my money to feed your armies. Why don't you tell me why I should listen to you?"

I drew breath and prepared to deliver my well-rehearsed pitch, at which point we were interrupted by the leisurely ladling of an ancient waiter who had arrived with a tureen of soup. You should know my table manners are not that good. I can't help it, but when I eat I am accused by my family of having an open food-filled mouth. My lack of fine motor skills means that at least half of the food I eat normally ends up on my shirt or trousers. I was not sure of protocol and after the debacle of 'no-tie-gate', I did not want to commit another affront to civilised society. I was torn between the fear of eating, knowing soup would be congealing on my designer stubble below my lips, and not eating, thereby delaying the flow of lunch. Should I slurp quickly between sentences or should I wait until I had finished my informal presentation and then down the bowl in one? All the contingency planning we had done as a team had not prepared me for this practical challenge, and in truth my performance was decidedly sub-par.

When I finished, there was temporary silence, punctuated by my frantic spooning of soup as I had decided to wait to the end to try to empty my bowl. Julian was unflappable, which was perhaps why he had chosen the prawn cocktail. One fork, five mouthfuls, thank you and goodnight. He rushed to my rescue, adding a couple of points I had omitted, and qualified some of my explanations. He concluded as the plates were cleared away.

"George, I know this is unfamiliar territory for you, but you've known me all my life and I think you have a sense of what I can achieve. The start-up world has changed now because of the invention of the smartphone. There are riches that can be accrued faster than any property development can be built. Investors are seeing that good ideas can go global in a matter of months. Tech companies reach a certain scale and then they invest in the innovation of others in case they can't develop the next innovation themselves. This is an idea that has it all, but what will make it successful is the skill and ambition of the people behind it. I know you believe in me. You need to believe in Alex. He's brimming with ideas and he knows how to build this venture. Take this plan and show it to one of your advisors. Check the numbers. You'll get excited too."

It was quite a speech. Lord Dobson swirled the dregs of his wine and stared at me with a look that was completely inscrutable. I had no sense of what was coming.

"Alex, you clearly have a fan in my godson. Tell me about yourself. Would I know your father?"

Hmmm. Stuart Lazarus, intellectual scourge of the Establishment, darling of the Left, happy to appear on any platform for the promotion of his latest work chronicling the iniquities of the capitalist hegemony. Not quite the calling card I needed right now.

"I don't think so, George. He's a teacher and my mother is a clinical psychologist." His brow furrowed, frowned and tightened. It was quite a talented brow.

"Where do you hail from?" he asked pointedly.

"Willesden," I replied, thinking that would close the conversation down.

"The Cricklewood or Kilburn end?" A tad specific, I felt, and wondered which was the better answer. "I have many apartment blocks on Willesden Lane," he added with a smile. I had inadvertently reminded him of his fortune, which I assumed was a good thing.

"And Alex, tell me, do you want to be famous or do you want to be rich?"

"I want to be successful, George. I want to create something that will make me feel proud that the effort has been worthwhile. I don't want to change the world, but I do want to make my presence felt." Good answer, I thought, and sensed that Julian was vigorously nodding alongside me.

Lord Dobson smiled and licked his lips, clearing the invisible remnants of his main course. He sat upright, shoulders pinned back, unruffled and superior. An enormous smile spread across his face and he clapped his hands like an overexcited football fan.

"Julian my boy, I like this fellow. A little graceless, of course, but full of enthusiasm and ideas. Precious commodities. We will review your numbers and get back to you within forty-eight hours with our decision and our conditions."

It was as easy as that. No difficult questions on the size of the market or the complexity of guaranteeing a sufficiency of sellers. The business was over, and the lunch became most agreeable, with a lot of indiscreet gossip from naughty Lord Dobson. He pointed out a Labour peer in the corner of the dining room, currently sleeping in his office because of a 'harmless clinch' with a twenty-two-year-old intern, which his provincial wife had needlessly seen as something serious. He dropped in nonchalantly over coffee that he had a meeting in the afternoon with the prime minister himself. He intended to tell him that the 'right-wing bastards' in the party must not push him to have a referendum on Europe in the next few years, no matter how strong the clamour. *For God's sake, you can't let the hoi polloi decide something that important for the country.*

* * *

Two days later, we had a very different meeting.

Still cold, the sky was a Mediterranean blue and London positively glistened. Julian, Dimitri and I marched purposefully from the street into the lobby of the uber-modern, gleaming St Martins Lane Hotel. We all wore jeans, and while Julian and I had smart open-necked shirts, Dimitri had his doctored Sex Pistols tee shirt, which had been adapted to read 'Anarchy in the Ukraine'. We took the lift to the penthouse and were greeted by two dark-suited security operatives with hybrid Israeli-Russian accents, who had, without doubt, killed many people in previous lives for sport. After frisking us with a vigour that seemed unnecessarily thorough, the door was opened, and we were brusquely shown in.

The suite was drenched in bright sunlight from the floor-to-ceiling windows overlooking Trafalgar Square. An iridescent gleam radiated from the strips of modern lighting concealed beneath various nooks in the wall. The room was set up to create a sense of discomfort and we were greeted by a wave of frantic chatter. Four or five people were walking around in tiny circles, shouting into their iPhones. Some were remonstrating in Hebrew and others fluently cajoling the poor person at the end of the line in aggressively accented English.

Moshe was sitting on a sofa with his feet on a glass table. He was all in black, wearing jeans and a tee shirt, and had matching cowboy boots with enormous heels. I hadn't seen boots like that for many years and thought they were impossible to buy outside of

Kansas these days, but I appreciated he may well have liked a trip to the rodeo in his spare time. On the table, there were two empty and one full espresso cups. He held a lit cigarette, ash drooping towards the pristine cream carpet. I didn't feel it was my place to remind him that this was probably a non-smoking penthouse.

He was, of course, also on the phone, talking with aggressive animation in Hebrew. He beckoned half-heartedly for us to sit down by him, which we did in polite silence. I tried to eavesdrop on his call, but my knowledge of Hebrew was largely synagogue-biblically based. He did not seem to be invoking that the children of Israel should leave Egypt, but I definitely made out the English phrase 'machine learning'.

After ten minutes in which we were ignored by everyone, Moshe abruptly ended his call and turned to us with a look of abstraction, asking indifferently: "Tell me, friends. Who are you and why are you here?"

I was about to reply when the door to the bedroom opened and out strode the tallest, most beautiful woman I had ever seen in the flesh. She was flawless and, to make concentration more compli-cated, she was wearing a swimming costume and a sarong, which seemed odd for late November in London. Moshe stood up and the need for cowboy boots with enormous heels became evident. He was still significantly shorter than her and, as he took her hand tenderly, I thought she was going to pat him affectionately on the head. They spoke in Hebrew. She was clearly modelling some new purchase and he was enraptured by his wife's beauty, which turned him into a fawning and distracted teenager.

Eventually the domestic sideshow came to an end and he ushered her back into the adjacent room, smirking with the smugness of someone for whom wealth had created opportunities that might not naturally have arisen.

He then turned to us without a trace of warmth and said simply, "Well, you haven't answered my question." Julian, snapping out of the reverie that a glimpse of an unexpected swimsuit model can create, started to talk rapidly.

"Thank you for seeing us, Moshe. I'm Julian Lloyd-Mason. I was your lawyer when you bought Capital Studios last year. You are apparently looking for investment in consumer brands with a global reach and we are going to create one."

Moshe looked at us as if we had threatened to kidnap his wife. He lit another cigarette, then turned to me and said, "You have three minutes. Go."

Adrenaline is a strange chemical when released. Fear can precipitate its creation, but as it starts to arrive, it then provides a temporary but impervious barrier to anxiety. This might be rubbish, but when I was given this narrow window to talk by a man of such superficial iciness, something kicked in and, if I say so myself, I was rather magnificent. In three minutes, I outlined the proposition, discussed the revenue model, told him why it would be successful. Finally, I asked him for a few million dollars he might have lying around.

Julian nodded so much in agreement that it must have looked like he was praying fervently. The thought did cross my mind that perhaps this was a test of our character, not our business idea. We had submitted the business plan to his lawyer in advance of the meeting, so we had assumed he had a scintilla of interest, otherwise he would have cancelled.

When I finished my declamation, he looked at the wall for a while and then spoke over his shoulder to one of the flunkies who had come off a call. This lasted another two or three minutes as we waited for some further acknowledgement. Finally, he looked at Julian and said in a staccato voice, like the rattle of a machine gun, "OK, Julian. Why would anyone listen to a lawyer?"

I suppose it was a good question to give someone in an entrance exam for law school, but not that relevant right now, as well as gratuitously rude. Julian was always calm. His upright posture remained militarily rigid and he smiled for an instant and then rather brazenly leant forward and put his hand on Moshe's shoulder. Neither of them flinched.

"Good question, Moshe. Here is my answer. Read our business plan and think of what we are trying to do. Parenting is the most important skill that comes with adulthood. We are going to make the world better at it. Too ambitious? Well then, half the civilised world, if we're being precise. Anywhere that people have a bit of money to buy a solution to a child's need. Yes, I'm a lawyer, but today you're meeting me as a businessman with a crackerjack idea that I'm willing to share with someone who hasn't the manners to shake our hands or offer us a drink. You can be as macho-wealthy as you like. It'll be your loss."

Julian sat back in his chair and smiled sweetly at Moshe. I felt very uncomfortable and shifted from one clenched buttock to the other. I was rather impressed by Julian's speech. We had too good an idea to be bullied by a little man dressed like Jon Voight in *Midnight Cowboy*.

Moshe stood up and motioned to one of the security guys, who moved his hand to his breast pocket and reached inside. That he had a gun, I had no doubt. That he was going to wave it at us seemed ridiculous. Instead, he and his boss started to giggle like idiots. Moshe beckoned me and Julian to stand up and he gave us big hugs, overpowering us with the fumes of his noxiously sweet and generously applied cologne.

"I am joking. I am sorry, I couldn't resist. People say Moshe Shalon has no sense of humour. You tell them differently, OK?"

I intended to tell everyone that he had a terrible sense of humour.

"And I treated you like shit, to see what you are like under pressure. I love your business plan. I want to give you a lot of money. We can do great things together. Why do you think you are here? To check out my wife?"

As if in a co-ordinated act, the door slid open and the lovely Ilana emerged in proper clothes and strode towards the door. She smiled at us sweetly and headed out. Perhaps she had been part of our character test? I don't know if we passed, but I would of course tell Sarah later that she looked weird up close and her neck was too long for her head.

"Come, come… Let's talk through the details. Sit with me and we'll make a plan." His people joined us at the table. Maybe they were part of the act too. I realised that the famous Avi Ram was not present as Moshe turned to Dimitri, who had remained seated in confused silence, and said, "Dimitri. We hear great things about you. You may be a genius like my Avi. We will have to see if you are as strange. Please go next door. Avi is waiting for you on Skype. He has some questions. If you can impress him, we will let you live." He laughed again at his own joke, as we remained stunned and silent.

Dimitri cracked his knuckles – a peculiar sign that he was about to do something technically brilliant – and trotted enthusiastically with one of the team to another little room. The door shut and we were left with an ebullient Moshe, who was growing more animated by the minute. What followed was a great conversation about our future and some very probing questions about our plan.

Like Lord Dobson before him, he promised us that he would resolve everything in a couple of days and told Julian to prepare for conversations with his lawyer. After a breezy hour, the door slid open and a jaunty Dimitri silently joined us, looking pleased with himself. Simultaneously, there was a loud ping from Moshe's phone, and he read the text immediately.

"It seems, Dimitri, that you have passed your interview. Avi thinks you are nearly as talented as he is."

* * *

By Christmas, we were set fair. We had over £6m in our bank account and a team of six people ready to conquer the world in the New Year. It had all happened so quickly. Lord Dobson and Moshe had agreed to give us £2.5m each. Aware of the other's existence, they had both tried to be the pre-eminent investor, but – keen to uphold Anglo-Israeli trading relationships – we didn't allow this to happen and insisted on parity.

The negotiations proceeded with surprising speed, although Moshe's team took pleasure in bombarding us with awkward and incessant questions. We found most of them unnecessary and they seemed more concerned with reminding us how tough they were to deal with, rather than the quality of our answers. A number of conditions were eventually imposed that proved non-negotiable, and we capitulated in haste to ensure we got their money quickly. We just wanted to get properly started.

Moshe wanted full access to all our data records and analytics, within the accepted jurisdictional constraints of EU law. We felt uncomfortable that this would lead to a commercial intimacy that was not usual, but we felt protected by law and common practice and did not want to lose either his money or his reputational support, which would count for so much in the tech world.

George Dobson had one immovable stipulation. He wanted to have a veto on any executive hiring we made, which was decidedly unusual, but this had to happen if we wanted to progress. 'Think of me as the American Constitution providing a few checks and balances. I am in the background and there to protect the people from voting for an idiot. You won't know I'm there.' I could see lots of disastrous future scenarios, but Julian tried to assuage my fears by constantly referencing his godfather's aim of 'supporting two bright lads and learning a bit myself along the way about the future'. Eventually I relented, realising that he needed to be able to have a level of intervention to satisfy his need for control. Days later, we toasted our future collective success with him over champagne at his club in town, and I even remembered my tie.

We took a further investment from a boutique VC called iSeed, having met a number of interested businesses, all of whom seemed equally keen. What swung it for us was their engaging enthusiasm allied with an encouraging lack of probing questions. They thought we were cool and although this was an unfamiliar description for me, they seemed easy to distract with our prodigious talent for spin.

We worked so hard that month. Fifteen-hour days, including the weekends, in a desperate attempt to get a Christmas and Boxing Day with our families. I was at home rarely and, even then, so focused that Santa and Mrs Claus could have come naked down the chimney, followed by enough elves to fill Wembley Stadium, and I would not have noticed.

Distracted, energised, and propelled by the rocket fuel of my unleashed ambition, I prepared for 2013. It was going to be phenomenal.

PART 2

GETTING GOING

7. Beginnings

When I look back on our hapless first months, I am amazed that we emerged from the chaos to build something tangible. There were so many things to accomplish and a never-ending series of challenges that we could never have anticipated, not to mention the regular cock-ups.

We started with an office of nine people. This included three interns who we had recruited from a graduate website with a listing that was perhaps a bit of an exaggeration in claiming we were voted 'The UK's Best Start-Up'. We expected them to lay down their lives to our cause. Indeed, Julian and I were so obsessed when we started that we blithely assumed that anyone who joined us would not mind foregoing the basic tenets of a social or family life.

Dimitri told us that he needed one person only to help him at the start, a young computer science graduate called Oliver, who was without doubt the shyest person I had ever met. Eye contact was a distant aspiration for him. Rather cruelly, he became known by the nickname 'Mumbles', reflecting his preferred mode of speech. Undeterred, Dimitri told us that in the anonymous online world of collaboration, Oliver was a rock star. A mute one, of course.

We sat in our open-plan industrial-chic loft with one meeting room, wittily called 'The Bored Room' to remind everyone that we were going to be a 'can do' rather than a 'can talk' sort of organisation. I had gone into mantra overdrive and the walls were awash with quotes and sayings that I had carefully curated after a vigorous Google search for 'Interesting quotes about Ambition'. Napoleon once said, for example: 'Great ambition is the passion of a great character. Those endowed with it may perform very good or very bad acts. All depends on the principles that direct them.'

I don't know why I wanted to quote Napoleon so much. Yes, he was emperor for a bit, but he died in exile in the middle of the South Atlantic and had a inferiority complex named after him.

There was also a lovely picture of Audrey Hepburn with the words 'Nothing is impossible, the word itself says I'm possible', which she allegedly once said, but no one quite knows why. *Roman Holiday* is one of my favourite films, romantic and impossibly elegant, which was my prompt. After a few months, however, Alice led a delegation of disgruntled female colleagues who demanded its removal on the grounds that it glibly suggested sexual availability.

Julian hated these posters, worrying that he was trapped in some whacky Californian cult of self-indulgent navel-gazing. I was more practical and considered it our role to lead by example. If we expected people to match our drive and desire for success, we needed to create an environment that would make everyone want to willingly give up their weekends too. A poster and a quote would surely do the trick.

Our early days were inauspicious. Simon incorporated the business incorrectly as 'PrimalParent', not 'PrimaParent'. This only came to light when we were approached after a couple of weeks by a weird community just outside of Brighton called 'Primal Earth Parents', who had a strange concept of looking after children based on a dubious practice called 'untethering'. They seemed to feel that we were a potential threat to their recruitment drive and sent us a very non-New-Age 'cease and desist' letter from a large firm of City lawyers.

In the first few months, we had clear areas of focus. Dimitri undertook to have a test site up and ready within three months, with a view to being fully operational two months later. Julian, assisted by Simon, worked on the financial planning and modelling and began to try to broker some commercial partnerships to support our launch. I drove our core proposition and the marketing plan. In particular, I looked at how we would recruit sellers on to the site and how I would drive subscriptions. Alice was Director in Charge of Cajoling and Shouting. She held us accountable to deliver what we said we were going to do on time. She also called out our bad behaviour or lack of integrity on a daily basis, as well as managing the infrastructure of a fledgling company – from recruitment, HR and bank accounts to toilet paper and coffee purchasing.

Dimitri's demeanour changed as soon as we started. He maintained the rigidity and obsessively structured approach to his working day, so you could watch him and over time work out his routine, down to the coffee breaks (9 a.m./11.30 a.m./2.30 p.m., and peppermint tea at 5.30 p.m.), as well as the loo trips an hour later. However, the effortless and arrogant disdain with which he dispatched projects previously was replaced with a much nastier streak that made him very difficult to deal with. Of the management team, he would only really talk to me as a necessary interface with the outside world. After about six weeks, he had an outburst that revealed his fragility.

Hovering by his desk, I attempted to make a bit of small talk, but to little avail. I could have performed the Macarena in a thong, and he wouldn't have looked at me. Eventually, I sort of whispered in his ear gently, "Dimitri, I really do need to get a sense of whether we are on track."

I did not expect what happened next. He didn't shout or scream. He covered his face with his hands and began a series of convulsive sobs, accompanied by a steady metronomic rocking. The sounds emanated from the darkest corners of his unfathomable soul. He said the same phrase in Russian over and over as the sobbing subsided. And then he stopped. A few deep breaths and he turned to me with a sardonic smile and simply said, "Thank you, Alex. The doubt is gone. Please go away and let me start."

I slunk away, confused. I had delivered a pep talk without actually saying anything and I was also none the wiser about timings. I realised that Dimitri saw our project as a route to elevating himself to immortality in the world of developers and engineers that was his natural habitat. He only cared about what would happen to his reputation among these people, not necessarily the commercial gain.

My first few months had a certain irony about them. I spent every waking moment immersed in searching out what was important for parents, obsessed and assiduous in my pursuit of solutions to everyday parenting dilemmas. But as a dad to Theo and Emily, not to mention as a husband to Sarah, I was a shadowy figure they occasionally bumped into in the house. I would leave for the office at 7 a.m. Emily had been an obliging child and slept through the night from a very early stage, and she and her brother woke about half an hour before I'd leave. I'd give them a quick cuddle in between checking my emails and writing notes to myself of shards with vague recollected thoughts, which seemed, at the time, crucial.

My day normally finished about 10 p.m. and I would stagger home exhausted, sustained by takeaways and prodigious caffeine intake. Sarah would be asleep in front of the TV or, more usually, in bed with an open book on her chest and her glasses on the tip of her nose. I would try to remove them gently, invariably poking her in the eye in doing so. She'd stir, smile wanly and say something like "Made us rich yet?", and then pull up the duvet and embrace sleep again. I promised her the weekends, but in truth I reneged and gave her only part of the weekends. I worked both days, and most Sundays popped into the office for a quick status update with the team. I did everything I could to play with the kids when I was home and I abandoned a social life and even my beloved Spurs to prioritise what little time I had for the family.

My whole family were casualties of this war against non-achievement I was waging. Judith and I were always very close, but our contact became intermittent. She was presiding over a rapidly growing organisation and at that time was increasingly pessimistic about the disastrous consequences of the Arab Spring for children across the region. While I was busy recruiting children's entertainers, she was monitoring the breakdown of civil order in Syria. I hardly listened when we did get together. I had deadlines to meet.

My parents were tolerant but resentful of my absence and crit-ical of its cause. They believed in a consistent calendar to preserve family unity: Friday night dinners and Sunday teas, birthdays and bank holidays. So when, for the second or third time running, I pitched up at ten to see plates being cleared and sleeping children being scooped into car seats, my mother looked coldly at me and quietly bemoaned, "I hope you think it's worth it, Alex." Sarah was silent and, at that moment, I wasn't so sure.

* * *

Julian encouraged the office to call me 'the Child Catcher' after the terrifying man with a net in *Chitty Chitty Bang Bang* who lures Jeremy and Jemima Potts into a cage with the promise of lollipops. My job was to find a whole host of entertainment for children and he thought it was hysterical to compare me to a character in a film that has given generations of young people (me included) unneces-sary nightmares. There was a serious point to the joke, and that was security, the reliability of the sellers we were recruiting, and the need for careful vetting and scrutiny.

We had many conversations about security initially. In creat-ing a vision for PrimaParent, we could sometimes forget that other people weren't as nice and scrupulous as us. All digital experience brands had faced the consequences and adverse effects of bad behaviour from customers and sellers. I became an expert in safe-guarding, something I had previously thought security guards did in banks. I even became certified in the subject (a thirty-minute online course one lunchtime, in which I aced the multiple choice). Fortunately, Alice did not flinch at the need for compliance and we put together a vetting process for future sellers who would come into direct contact with children.

We wanted to establish at the outset the sort of company that would attract the best people. Despite our inbuilt cynicism, Julian and I respected that we needed to marry a sense of fun with the commitment and hard work we expected from everyone. Julian was definitely quite old-fashioned in his approach and felt that a ping-pong table, lots of free alcohol and the prospect of inter-company illicit relationships would do the trick. I knew we needed to be perhaps a bit more adept in how we set about creating our culture.

One of the first team meetings we had was about ensuring that our company values befitted our company mission so that we would appear responsible grown-up parents, even if in truth we were probably as mature as reckless teenagers. There was inevitably tension between us as to why we were doing this. 'Values' for Julian were what stocks and shares have, but for Alice and some of the interns, we couldn't function as an organisation without them. I just wanted to get something agreed and move on.

We debated them endlessly and they seemed to have an organic life of their own, mutating like a nasty disease and evolving every time we had a conversation. Julian felt we should focus on success and his language was masculine and aggressive. He suggested we should be 'Dynamic, Unrelenting and Profit Focused' – not the best description to give a parent, perhaps. Alice suggested 'Nurturing, Empathetic and Intuitive'. I showed the draft to Julian, who by this time would not engage directly in the conversation. 'Not on my watch' was his caustic reply.

I shuttled between the different evolving factions in our tiny office like an optimistic UN peacekeeper, and feigned sincerity as I solicited clashing opinions. It became a battle of wills, as ever, between a righteous Alice and a cynical Julian. Remember, this all took place in our first months of working together, but it seemed the questioned values signified so much more, reflecting our individual moral codes.

Words lost all rightful meaning. I was involved in a two-day multi-media conference (phone, text, email, face-to-face) as to the interpretation of the word 'direct'. Did we mean in-your-face-say-it-as-it-is direct, or simply that we got things done with straightforward efficiency? Peace in the Middle East seemed a more likely occurrence than agreement at PrimaParent. I could take my role as corporate Kofi Annan no more, and so I sat at my computer and, on a single sheet of paper, I typed:

Enthusiastic. Creative. Kind.

I grabbed Alice, Julian, Simon and Dimitri and a couple of the interns and slammed the paper on the meeting room table.

"Well, I know I am enthusiastic, creative and kind. Now, do you muppets want to actually achieve anything?"

Everyone nodded obediently. Alice looked on the cusp of a contribution, but I looked at her and tried to convey a clear sense that if she disagreed, I'd dissolve the company. In the end our debate had fizzled due to lack of shared vision, so my catch-all and inoffensive suggestion filled the necessary gap. Values are all lovely, of course, but what we really needed to focus on was getting customers and sellers sorted.

8. Hacking at Growth

There was no point attracting people to the site if there was nothing to keep them there when they arrived. Before we launched, we had to find an endless supply of people, products and services that could make a trip to PrimaParent worthwhile. Having given it much thought during the whole planning period, we realised that we were going to have to be very clever about how we went about this task. For months, like it was a complicated military campaign in need of rigorous planning, General Lazarus thought of little else. Imagine the war room in Churchill's bunker with tanks being pushed around a map.

First of all, we needed to do a bit of old-fashioned research and compile a list to end all lists potential of sellers for the site. In our first week, I sat down with our most experienced intern, twenty-three-year-old Razia, a recent economics graduate, and briefed her. We sat by the coffee machine at a café table we had bought from Argos and I made her a flat white. I felt that a lovingly prepared cup of coffee from me could get anyone to do my bidding. Bloody millennials apparently don't drink regular milk, though, and you try getting a decent froth from yucky soy or almond milk.

Razia was unbelievably keen and would say 'That's so exciting!' to any task given to her. I had a project akin to counting grains of sand on a beach. As she stared at me with a commitment to dedicating her young life to the service of our start-up, I anticipated her face crumpling when I delivered her assignment.

"Razia, I need you to recruit a team of a couple more willing victims and then you all have three weeks to compile the biggest database you will ever prepare. I want every children's entertainer, party planner, caterer, bouncy castle inflator, clown, present-maker, toy manufacturer, tennis coach, circus skills trainer, personal tutor, wrapping paper manufacturer. You get the picture. We need them by postcode, and we need them for the whole country."

"Oh my God, that is so amazing!" Well, I didn't see that coming. Not even the vaguest expression of fear or suggestion of being daunted by this Herculean data-gathering exercise. She picked up her coffee, desperate, it seemed, to get started. "I have a couple of friends who we can get in and they'll love this. Can we pay them, although I'm sure they'll do it for the experience?"

I was thrilled that we had found such willing cannon fodder and told her that money was of course available, as was a hotline to Domino's Pizza at all hours. We didn't speak again for the next few weeks, but if I looked in her direction, she would give me a thumbs up and then bury her head once more in her laptop. She was quickly joined after this briefing by nameless friends recruited to the task. They never really left the office for three weeks and sat rooted to their computers, emanating an odour of intense effort combined with poor personal hygiene.

They, of course, did an exemplary job and we had a database of nearly fifteen thousand names in the allotted period. The achievement was significant. Three people working a fourteen-hour day, seven days a week, producing five thousand names each. That works out at about two hundred and thirty names a day or seventeen names an hour or a new name entered into our records every three minutes. That list gave us a foundation of contacts to build on and became the rather cumbersome manual methodology we used when we rolled out across international markets.

Armed with this database, we developed a plan to announce ourselves with a flourish. Julian and I realised early on that we had to be noisier and more brazen in our attempts to get noticed. In one of our earliest conversations, we had divided up responsibilities for how we would go about being brash and opportunistic in how we marketed ourselves. I was charged with recruiting a creative 'council of war' of talented individuals, primarily from the advertising industry, who could generate ideas, make films and help us get noticed. Julian, it transpired, had a very impressive black book of entertainment contacts, from actors to agents and producers, garnered from both his legal career and years of basically being well connected. We had a bit of a head start.

* * *

Strategy and planning are of course essential, but the overriding ingredient to our success was much more ephemeral. We were lucky. This manifested itself sometimes in not getting destroyed when things went wrong, as they frequently did. Primarily, however, we had two enormous dollops of divine intervention that we could not have anticipated. Dollop one was down to Julian's connections.

I had convened a group of designers and writers who agreed to moonlight for us. In turn, I promised them eventual equity in the business, which would make them squillionaires. They were led by Frank and Frankie, a married creative team who worked together with great success, illustrated by the many awards displayed on their mantelpiece at home. Full of ideas, they were either bickering constantly or simpering over one another like teenagers.

At our first gathering, I briefed them to come up with an idea for a film that would make the world talk about us before we had actually done anything or even launched. I reminded them we were loath to spend the money we had just secured, so we had to pull in favours and freebies. They disappeared back to their day jobs, and a couple of days later Julian and I were chatting over coffee when he suddenly announced, "You know, I completely forgot to say, Charlie Evans told me that he was happy to help us however we need."

"Not Charlie Evans, the comic actor star of *Baby Boomers*?" I asked with incredulity. You will remember that, by then, it was about Series 3. It had become a major hit in the US. Charlie was hotter than boiling water. "How the hell do you know him?" I continued.

"You remember when he was caught for possessing Class A drugs?"

"No?"

"Exactly. He had an amazing lawyer. Got him off and kept it out of the papers. He told me the other day that he'll appear in a promotional film, anything we want."

"You couldn't have remembered this when we briefed everyone the other day?"

"I admit, not my brightest moment. We should probably tell them, shouldn't we?"

"Oh, my word, I am working with an incompetent. Of course we should tell them. We can make a film with one of the biggest stars in the UK. This is the biggest slice of luck imaginable." I called Frank and Frankie immediately, but they sounded unimpressed.

"Well, we could use him, but we might want to do something clever with animation instead," Frankie informed me. Not the reaction I had expected. I pointed out that they would have to march over my dead body before we produced a promotional cartoon rather than utilising this incredible opportunity.

Clearly, they valued me alive, because a few days later they came to the office giggling with enthusiasm and announced to Julian and myself that they had solved the problem and we could after all create an amazing film fronted by Charlie Evans. Julian and I smiled at each other and thanked them profusely for their creative flexibility. The idea was very simple and did not change very much from the original script to the finished film.

Charlie played the worst parent in the world. Lots of snippets of him doing things badly. Reading a bored toddler *Great Expectations*, preparing a tea of quinoa-based elaborate salads for a number of kids, dragging recalcitrant children round an art gallery full of esoteric modern art, watching them unwrap birthday presents of random irrelevant and inappropriate items (from garish ties to bottles of fine wine to random antiques), and finally watching black-and-white subtitled French films with a snoozing child. It was the perfect and obvious use of a celebrity famed for sharp British wit and foppishness wrapped in a personality lacking self-awareness. There were two simple title screens at the end:

Soon there will be a better way to parent.
PrimaParent.com. Family First

Making the film was a surprisingly smooth process. Charlie was on a break between series and coerced his team to work for free, including the director. We shot over two long days in March and kept costs down to a minimum. Charlie was very funny, facial expressions and ad libs creating this persona of a well-intentioned but clueless parent. Without really too much trouble, our un-launched and customer-free business had an advertising campaign that could be global in its reach. I told you it was a big dollop of luck.

We now had to disseminate our message to an unsuspecting world.

* * *

Growth. Growth. Growth. It's all start-up businesses worry about. How many new customers, how many new likes, how much more engagement with our website or downloads of our app? It is interesting that 'personal growth' is about making us better human beings, looking at our weaknesses and fears and making progress in countering them. 'Corporate growth' in the digital age is about eyeballs and sign-ups. Money is raised, an online presence is created, and driving the quest for global domination is a twenty-first century dark art: growth hacking. Dimitri and I were responsible for devising tactics, scrupulous or not, to generate sign-up of customers and sellers. I would think of what we needed, and he would execute the technical sleight of hand to ensure its delivery. There were a number of strands of activity.

We had our launch film. The first job was to get it out quickly. We were lucky, of course, that not only was Charlie very famous, but he had an unhealthy and sometimes inappropriate obsession with Twitter and therefore a huge following. On 2 May, we got him to tweet the film with the message 'Très Amusant'. (Not our choice, but he wanted to do it in his own style.) Julian made a number of phone calls to his coterie of influencers and got them to do the same thing. We also sent the film to Moshe with the brief 'Can Avi get this out there?' We chose not to ask too many questions about the methods he was going to use.

By 16 May, we had over two million views on YouTube and that figure rose significantly by the end of the month. Most people just watched the film, but over 4 per cent of the views clicked through to the newly launched site. Dimitri built in lots of clever cookies and traps that meant if you did not register, we knew where to find you and could come back in full force to make sure you did not escape.

Within the first five weeks, we managed to get fifty thousand registrations of interest from customers and, most importantly, just under two thousand potential sellers. This was cemented by an email campaign to the huge list compiled by Razia, which one might call more of a bombardment. OK, so we were a little bit lax in securing consents and opt-ins. But at that time, we confidently felt that there were likely to be few future consequences.

Concurrently, Dimitri got to work on making sure we appeared everywhere through a very aggressive search strategy. Somewhere in

time, marketing a product had changed from making sure that someone saw your advertisement to being sure you advertised yourself to
anyone that expressed an interest in your category by typing a search
request into Google. The industry had transformed dramatically and
what made you rich and famous was your ability to bend the Google
algorithm to serve your own needs. We knew we had to be very clever
in making sure that if you made the vaguest enquiry about a parenting need, we were the obvious solution that was offered.

Our ethics were further challenged by Dimitri one day a few
weeks into our hacking. He asked to see me and Julian privately and
started with a question neither of us expected.

"What would you say if I told you that we have access to the
customer data of a major retailer and the largest online greetings
card business? So many potential customers."

"How is that possible?" I asked with incredulity.

"Let's just say I know some people. Completely untraceable. No
identity. Basically, they live underground in countries you will never
visit." Julian, as ever, was inscrutable. He seemed intrigued by the
revelation but did not smile.

"It's illegal, Dimitri," he said. "You could go to prison."

Dimitri smiled and winked at Julian as if to say, *what a quaint
and impossible eventuality*. He replied with a palpable smirk.

"You are very naive. Do you not think the world's most
encrypted data is available for a price? This has no cost attached.
Someone is helping me because I once helped her."

"Favours can come at a price, Dimitri. Are you sure that we
could contact people and our methods would be untraceable?"

"Julian, you are a nice guy. I should take you on a tour of the
dark web. This is nothing. Alex, why are you not saying anything?"

I was silent because I was torn between an impulse to seize this
opportunity and an awareness that it would be wrong to do so. I

mean, it was hardly a major crime. We'd send out some messages to people who could choose to ignore them. The transgression was really a matter of principle derived from who actually owned some data. And because the digital world is out of control, our data is clearly susceptible to being purloined or hacked by someone. Conversely, had I started a business founded on supposedly being a better human being, only to lose perspective on what should be a clear moral decision?

I was rapidly turning into Hamlet deliberating the question of 'to breach or not to breach'. By now, Julian had made up his mind about a course of action and was expecting me to agree. Driven by a realisation that to get where you need to you have to overlook the odd principle, I nodded my head and simply said, "We never talk about this again. Julian and I know nothing about what might be about to happen. *Capisce?*"

"*Capisce*," Julian replied.

Dimitri looked at me enigmatically.

"I wish I understood what you are talking about most of the time, Alex."

* * *

These early days were really just about creating fame. If you call someone a 'hack', you are suggesting they are only interested in writing for money, with little artistic integrity. But call someone in a start-up business a 'growth hacker' and you are marvelling at their opportunism and skill. We were very proud of our cavalier disregard for probity and ethics in acquiring new customers. Our aim was simply to get noticed by as many people as possible. Fame was generated by our film with Charlie and its immediate ubiquity. It was enhanced by the volume of data we mysteriously had to play with. We realised, however, that PR was about so much more, and we needed to create some ideas, stunts and events that announced our arrival.

Big time.

9. Self-Publicising

Dodging the summer rain, I wearily trotted into the office, tired and lacking energy after a particularly punishing few days. As I entered, the mood seemed subdued and the room went silent for a moment, as if everyone was trying to hide something from me. Julian hadn't arrived yet, but Alice saw me and came running up clutching a tabloid.

"You'd better see this. We've made the paper."

"Already? That's amazing," I shouted, and gave what can only be described as an extremely badly co-ordinated fist pump. Alice shook her head wearily and handed me a copy of the *Mirror*.

There was a large colour photo of a very cute ringleted girl, flanked by her parents, with the doleful expressions of a family whose pet hamster has been accidently flushed down the loo. The headline read:

DID SOMEONE ORDER A BOOZY CASTLE?

A drunken delivery driver working for the appropriately named company 'Bouncy Mayhem' had got into a fight with Tabitha's grandfather and run amok among the jelly and ice cream until his arrest, which became a quasi-siege as he crouched behind the fairy castle claiming to be armed (with a hand-pump only, it transpired). Tabitha's incensed father knew a journalist and hence the story ran on an otherwise quiet news day. The article concluded with the disastrous sentence:

We contacted PrimaParent and a spokesman commented, 'I don't know what the fuss is about. The reservation system worked perfectly.

I suddenly felt even more exhausted.

"Who took the call from the newspaper and gave that idiotic comment?" I shouted with unfamiliar anger in my voice. There must have been a mouse scuttling across the room, because suddenly everyone was staring intently at their feet. After a moment of silence, Dimitri piped up from behind his bank of computer screens.

"I spoke to someone from some paper. Why?"

Suddenly all became clear. And terrifying.

"Dimitri, what on earth did you say?"

He looked bemused. "I told them that our site did what it is meant to do. It recommended someone for a party and facilitated the reservation. Why is it our problem if the man got drunk and started a fight?"

I suppose I was grateful that at least further investigation wasn't necessary, as the smoking telephone was in Dimitri's hand. Angry father informs journalist friend who speaks to emotionally incontinent but genius chief technical officer. There was only one outcome possible.

Julian arrived shortly afterwards and frowned as he read the article. We sat with Alice in The Bored Room and debated our response. We did have a couple of enquiries from other journalists and ensured that the calls came to me. I wrote a short statement about how upset we were and that the only memories we wanted to create were happy ones. We decided to buy our way out of trouble. We ordered Tabitha the most expensive fairy princess costume we could find, hand-sewn by magic pixies and enchanted squirrels. I personally took it round to her, a good move as it placated her father and he even let me take a picture of Tabitha, looking like a slightly bemused Tinker Bell. The case of fine wine we also purchased shut Mum and Dad up most effectively.

We knew we had to tough it out and turn this experience into a lesson in how to manage an unintended and inevitable consequence of the quest for fame. Julian said to me several days later, as the pressure subsided, "Well, it could have been worse."

"I suppose the delivery bloke could have thrown up on Tabitha."

"Not quite what I meant," Julian continued. "Have you seen how website traffic has spiked since the article?" I hadn't actually checked, and he was right. We had seen a huge increase in people not just visiting but engaging with us.

"I think Dimitri could be an asset in more ways than we thought." Tact and diplomacy were clearly overrated.

* * *

Awareness, fame, curiosity – ours was not a complicated PR strategy. We were well-networked, but we had to be loud and obnoxious as often as was possible. This initial piece of adverse publicity was actually in stark contrast to the rave PR we had been receiving.

First, we decided to have an enormous launch party at Soirée, the nightclub Julian had a small stake in. We got quite carried away with planning a very cool and chic late-night gathering that would be crammed full of celebrities, journalists, bloggers and influencers enjoying our alcohol-fuelled largesse. The party planner (a friend of Julian's, of course) was due to come in with initial ideas, when Alice caused us to reconsider. She had not been involved and made an obvious point we had overlooked.

"Look, boys, far be it from me to interrupt your attempt to recreate Woodstock or the last days of the Roman Empire, but I think you are missing something quite important."

"Oh, I doubt that, Alice," Julian retorted with an arrogance that suggested successful social events were exclusively his domain.

"Since we're a parenting website, my view is that we should be more Harry Potter than Freddie Mercury in theme. At the very least, it has to be during the day and full of kids. You know,

Julian, little adults." We indeed should have thought it through a bit better.

"Sorry," I ventured cautiously, "but she's right. We do need kids, cake and jelly. We'll just have to return the vodka fountain."

Julian nodded. It was a rare moment of cohesion between us all and we started to refocus our planning efforts. He slapped her on the back, like she was one of the chaps, and declared: "Alice, we'd be lost without your common sense. This is going to have to be a kids' party that'll have the little buggers fighting each other to get in. And I mean properly punching and kicking, not just a bit of shoving."

We decided to make it a Sunday lunchtime. The guest list was what you might describe as charmingly eclectic. Julian and I invited our families and various friends and their kids to make up the numbers. We had a lot of minor celebrities from reality shows whom I did not really recognise. They were lovely to look at but seemed rather out of place, insisting on selfies with toddlers who were oblivious to their fame. The children were in turn intrigued and slightly spooked by their artificial noses and lips, which seemed likely to collapse or melt at any time. There were also journalists and TV presenters with their offspring, mingling awkwardly with a few well-known footballers and sports personalities. Charlie Evans couldn't come, but we had a couple of the cast of *Baby Boomers* whom he had gently suggested should attend, unless they wanted to be written out of Series 4.

Sarah came up to me at some stage in the afternoon and whispered, "Oh, look at you, Alex Lazarus, friend to the rich and famous. I hope you'll remember your kith and kin from the suburbs who were always there for you when you were a bit of a nonentity."

"Security. Security. I am being hounded by a madwoman. Have her removed."

"Alex. You may have forgotten us all. But I am very proud." She squeezed my hand.

'Sorry, I wasn't joking. I really am getting security. It's important I have no emotional ties to drag me down. Sorry, love, but good luck with the doctor thing and say hi to the kids."

As soon as I said this, I winced at my lack of tact, but as ever Sarah let it pass. She wandered back to my parents, who were looking after the kids. They were gracious, if slightly bemused. My father was socially adept at striking up and maintaining a witty conversation with anyone. Sharquisha, recent winner of *Your Day in Court*, was proving a bit of a challenge. (You got to be the judge of a matrimonial dispute, with barristers and expert witnesses. My father refused to accept it was legally binding.)

Catherine seemed subdued and sat with friends in the corner nursing a constant glass of wine, vaguely supervising her brood. She and Julian hardly acknowledged each other for the duration of the afternoon. I tried to speak to her, though it was like engaging with a disgruntled teenager attending a granny's birthday party. Julian did interact with his kids a bit, but I got the sense that they were a useful prop in his arms when he was talking to someone influential, to reinforce his credentials as an all-round top bloke. They were a very photogenic family and the one group shot that Catherine participated in made them all look like catalogue models. My kids cultivated a sort of rustic dishevelled look that had the effect of keeping any photographer at bay.

The key was to have opinion formers and influencers generate lots of interest – individuals with significant fan bases and followers, who commented on parenting and indeed made significant income through the promotion of their knowledge or the cutesiness of their children. We picked the best and most interesting sellers and encouraged them to join in the fun.

There were some fabulously inventive individuals on display. You could design your own jigsaw, make funky socks and learn incredible card tricks. We had singing and dancing teachers and Yoga for Tots (a woman called Dagma, who basically got them to sing 'Head, Shoulders, Knees and Toes' repeatedly). Star attraction was the UK champion face painter, a heavily tattooed woman from Coventry who was an artist with both a needle and a make-up brush. We made sure she used the latter.

She worked her magic on one of the footballers, himself no stranger to a bit of ink on his arms. The England midfielder had played away quite a lot recently and his wife was giving him one last chance to improve his home form. He was therefore totally pliant and playing the role of doting parent to the full. His wronged missus seemed to relish briefing his face painting and, after an hour, the artwork was very impressive. It was a magnificent photo opportunity, and to help you imagine the design, I will simply tell you the headline in the *Sun* the following day:

THREE LIONS ON HIS SHIRT, BUT SUCH A PRETTY KITTY ON HIS FACE.

We couldn't have hoped for better coverage, as the photo went global with our branding clearly displayed behind him. The whole afternoon was unquestionably very successful. People had fun and with the exception of the little boy who, unable to find the loo, relieved himself by the shapely ankles of a humourless newsreader, there were few mishaps. Julian and I made a welcome speech, which we had rehearsed carefully. We outlined why we were committed to changing how people parented and talked about our mission and purpose. We even thanked our lovely wives, one of whom was smiling and the other scowling. We finished in a jokey fashion.

Me: "Well, who knows, Julian, what we'd both be doing if we hadn't started talking in the park that day?"

Julian: "You'd still be in a boring office making bad jokes."

Me: "And you'd be a boring lawyer always out at lunch."

Julian: "Thank the Lord we found each other."

Yes, we were that hilarious.

* * *

Our opening few months were about stunts and getting coverage. I did a deal with Out There PR, a young agency who spotted in us the chance to make a name for themselves. They agreed to do the first three months for a future bonus in lieu of payment now and, in return, I agreed that we would not veto their ideas if they felt particularly strongly about something.

I knew the two principals, Max and Louise, from when we were all formerly employed at larger agencies and had shared a client. They had bravely given it all up to do their own thing, telling me at the time that their ambition wasn't necessarily to make a fortune, but to be responsible for the decisions they made for themselves. PR had evolved. It was no longer boozy champagne lunches with journalists in return for column inches. Now you needed to create content and narratives in social media communities, to be disseminated by people you didn't know. Certainly, the industry didn't require you to dress as if you were going shopping in Knightsbridge. This was lucky for Max and Louise, who didn't care about an elegant wardrobe and looked like they were about to do the gardening.

Gathered in The Bored Room, they enthusiastically went through some of their initial ideas, which included a 'parent of the year' competition. Max grandly proclaimed:

"We've done our research, and there are lots of worthy awards, but not one that is contemporary and would attract a national media partner. We get nominations from all over the country, a few celebrities to help endorse it, and a newspaper or radio station for coverage, which would be easy to do. The key is to use it as a vehicle to tackle the issues of what it takes to be a parent today."

"It's not really that original, is it?" I ventured as politely as I could.

Max shrugged his shoulders and declared, "What is really 'new' these days? The important thing is not the idea, but the way you make it happen." Louise broke a chilly atmosphere by feigning to vomit at her partner's platitudes.

Julian, who had been staring out of the window with evident indifference, perked up considerably and started to scroll through his phone contacts to enlist support. After a short debate, the consensus was that if we focused all our effort around a big event, we could probably create a property that we could own in perpetuity. If perpetuity was too long a milestone, then certainly the next year would do. I was excited by the idea and safe in the knowledge of one thing. With the amount of time Julian, Alice and I were spending in the office, none of us was going to win the competition.

* * *

Things moved pretty fast from there. When our PR representatives pitched 'PrimaParent of the Year' to a number of potential media partners, there was a lot of immediate interest and in the end a national newspaper agreed to get behind the project.

It all had to be done without a physical awards ceremony. We did not want to hire an anonymous function room in a large Central London hotel and hope that enough tables were sold to break even. Instead, we had the lovely idea to livestream the event from our offices, which, with a bit of dressing, we could make look like an ultra-cool soft-play area with a funky bar. We decided to build everything round a gigantic futuristic ball pond surrounded by café tables filled with family and friends. Adroit camerawork would make the whole thing look bigger, while ensuring at the same time that the photocopier and paper shredder were well out of shot. The effect was certainly distinctive – a sort of Whacky Warehouse meets Shoreditch Drug Den. Very on-brand.

The first problem arose twenty minutes before transmission. Sarah had brought the kids and they were giggling naughtily as they played in the ball pond. The broadcast director became tetchy and asked if they could get out so he could complete his checks. We had decided to conduct parent interviews in the ball pond to be unconventional. As Sarah lifted Emily, I noticed that her little cream tights were a rather muddy shade of brown. Sarah immediately flinched as she realised that our daughter had suffered what we expert parents call 'a catastrophic nappy malfunction'. Sarah was staring at the ball pond as if she had dropped a contact lens. I sidled up to her conspiratorially and whispered nonchalantly out of the corner of my mouth, "What's up?"

Sarah, professional unflappable healthcare professional that she was, leant towards me and quietly observed, "Our daughter has shat in the ball pond." Almost in comic unison, we peered down and I thought I could see a small offending smear of excrement on a yellow plastic ball.

"It could be everywhere!"

This was not the sort of reception we had intended for our parental role models. I needed to get the ball pond cleared of any lingering contents of Emily's loose nappy. Not the sort of task for which there is an automatic queue of willing volunteers. But that is why we have interns. You'll recall Razia and her friends, who compiled our initial database? They were sitting in the corner drinking coffee and looking mildly disdainful at the intrusion of strangers into their safe office space. I broke the news to Razia, the ever-willing volunteer.

"Razia, grab a couple of people and get in the ball pond and start wiping all the balls. My daughter has done a number two in there."

(I thought it best to keep it vaguely mathematical.) As soon as I said it, I realised that this was likely to be one of the stranger requests I would make in the office. Razia, ever compliant and unfailingly industrious, smiled at me and simply said, "She's your daughter. You do it."

There was little time to argue and so I jumped into the infected area like a brave firefighter. Sarah passed me a muslin and I frantically started sifting through the thousands of balls as if cleaning them all in five minutes was a realistic possibility. Focused on the job (or more precisely the big jobbie), I became aware of Julian standing by the side of the ball pond, arms folded, with a vaguely amused and sardonic expression.

"Honestly Alex, you pick your moments to behave like a child!"

* * *

Fortunately, our finalists were being briefed elsewhere during the cleaning up operation, so they willingly got into the ball pond to be interviewed as the transmission began and were unperturbed by the high levels of sniggering from the audience. There were three who had made it through quite a lengthy screening process. We had received over five thousand entries, each one containing a five-hundred-word submission. They had all been moving testaments to modern parenting challenges and we used a lot of the content for subsequent PR activity, when we wanted to talk about how families were changing. Mr Clive Riordan from Basingstoke, however, did not take the competition as seriously as we would have hoped and sent us a picture of his portly naked frame, holding a handwritten sign reading 'Who's the Daddy?' Not quite what we meant.

Our finalists all had moving stories to tell about superhuman feats of parental care, but there was a clear winner. Hankies at the ready.

Corporal Jack Elliot was thirty years old and had been in the Paras since he was eighteen. The regiment motto is *Utrinque Paratus*, translated as 'Ready for Anything', but Jack was not prepared for the overwhelming emotional impact fatherhood had on him. He had married his first girlfriend, Jane, when he was eighteen. All he wanted was to be a father, but years of trying resulted only in heartbreak for the couple. The complexity of receiving fertility treatment combined with Jack's tours of duty in terrifying war zones made his domestic life very stressful, but Jack was a kind and loving husband. Two years ago, Jane miraculously found herself pregnant, despite the prevailing pessimism of the many doctors they had visited. Baby William arrived and Jack did not think he could be any happier. When William was only seven months old, Jack was sent to Afghanistan for his second tour of duty and his world was shattered.

It was particularly dangerous in Helmand in 2012 and, despite his training and years of brave service, Jack grew terrified that something would happen to him and he would not see William again. He became obsessed with ensuring that if anything bad occurred, his son would know who he was and what he believed. He began to record his thoughts on anything and everything on his phone. It was a simple attempt to codify his feelings and he called it 'For William, with Love'. Observations, emotions, cultural references, jokes – anything he could think of. Whenever a signal allowed, he would send another digital file back to Jane to transcribe. He decided to illustrate each chapter, being a very competent artist, and the twelve completed personalised sketches became the visual representation of his love for his son.

He had just finished a thirteenth when he was suddenly called on patrol one evening. He didn't have time to return the sketch to the safety of his locker and carefully folded it and placed it in his inside pocket. Some twenty minutes later, his jeep came under fire from the Taliban. Jack survived but was shot in the leg. Traumatised and debilitated, he managed to return home to William and vowed never to leave his side. He was now publishing his book and was the primary carer for William as he learnt to live with the physical and emotional scars of his injury.

Jack was the last candidate in the ball pond for his interview, which in hindsight was perhaps an error because of the discomfort it caused him entering and exiting. When he finished telling his story in a soft West Country burr, tears were streaming down cheeks and stifled sobs were followed by quiet applause. He became the coveted winner of the first 'PrimaParent of the Year' trophy.

Like all our early victories, it was the newsworthiness of the stories we generated that helped facilitate a dramatic impact. Our media partner ran a spread the next day with the emotive headline 'Meet the UK's Greatest Dad' and used the observations of Jack's book to start a debate about what wisdom we should impart to our children. Our association with this national conversation meant that traffic to our site continued ahead of our expectations. It was accompanied by an increase in interest in Julian and me as the founders of this new, noisy online brand. Suddenly, we had to think about our own profile.

* * *

Interview requests started to come in from a host of different sources. Beginning with the digital and marketing press, where we were treated as a curious start-up with a penchant for PR, it was the newsworthiness of our events that quickly attracted interest from the nationals. One morning I received a call from the business editor at *The Times* asking permission to send a journalist and photographer to cover us for a feature for an upcoming Saturday edition.

"I think we've captured something. They like us because we're trying to make a difference," I told Julian over coffee.

"Do you really think so?"

"Yes," I continued, with my normal over-heightened need to make a speech. "I really do think we have a purpose. That's why so many people seem to want to help us."

"No, that's not what I meant. I know we have a purpose, it's just mine is a bit more commercially focused than yours. Do you think we are doing this interview because we've done something noble?"

"Well, what else?"

"George Dobson rang the editor and told him to do it. Apparently, he had some rather compromising evidence to trade on a cabinet minister who was proving rather disloyal. Something to do with losing a custody battle because of a nasty alcohol problem. So yes, it was parenting that got us the interview. Just not the type of parenting we are meant to be advocating."

"You think I'm very naive, don't you?"

"Charmingly so."

"That's why we're such an effective team. I see the good in people and you try to attack it."

Julian nodded as if I had said something profound. He then concluded: "I suppose we need to work out what we want to say in the interview. As long as I do all the talking and am in front of you in the picture, we'll be fine."

* * *

I'm a bit embarrassed to admit that I went shopping to prepare for the interview. There was going to be a posh photographer and I wanted to look the part. After debate with Alice and some of the interns, I felt I should look like I was 'Cool Dad at Home' – jeans and a tee shirt, with a creative twist. Rummaging through some rails at a rather grimy Shoreditch store, I found a white tee shirt with the famous picture of a scruffy Albert Einstein sticking his tongue out. Elegantly styled with some Levi's 501s and white Converse baseball boots, I arrived in the office ready to represent the youthful on-trend-cool-funky-down-to-earth-chic-but-approachable look that I had effortlessly created.

From the other side of the office, Julian appeared, dressed as if he was a guest of a minor royal at a polo match. He had on cream chinos, a blue blazer and a white linen shirt, with a polka-dot pocket square. He looked very handsome and dapper, two adjectives you might have struggled to use for me.

"When are you getting dressed for the interview?' he enquired sternly.

"I am dressed. Someone needs to create the impression we are a tech business, not a firm of stockbrokers."

Alice, who had witnessed the clash of fashion cultures, was enjoying the spectacle. "Honestly, Julian, you look lovely. If I didn't like women, I could fall for you big time. Can I see your yacht someday?"

I sniggered, but she didn't want to let me off the hook either: "And Alex. Don't you need to get back to your bedroom and listen to your Nirvana records? Listen, boys, stop trying so hard and perhaps speak to each other before you plan your wardrobes for your next appearance."

Before we could respond, the metallic groan and strain of the antique lift announced the imminent arrival of the interview team, and before we could art-direct our appearance further, we were being photographed against differing industrial and pipe-laden backgrounds in a series of incongruous and unsustainable poses. Our interviewer was an edgy youthful journalist, James Connor, who was clearly something of a rising star. He was smartly dressed, clean-shaven and extremely articulate. His questions were delivered with staccato shrillness, as if grinding out an admission of guilty complicity from us. For what, I don't know.

"So, how did the idea develop?" he opened. I prepared to launch into the random serendipity of our sandpit encounter.

Julian, sensing the imminent revelation of extraneous information, cut in without hesitation.

"Alex and I had been mulling over a number of start-up ideas for some time and we felt that parenting had enormous commercial scope."

"Yes," I added, "we wanted to make a difference to people's family lives."

Julian was leaning forward, straining to take command of the conversation. He clearly didn't trust me to not rhapsodise about our mission, but I wasn't going to give him the satisfaction of muzzling my passion.

"And in difficult times, spreading a little bit of happiness is not a bad reason to come into work." My answer must have really niggled Julian and I tried not to smile. I had clearly done something, because his next reply came in a voice at least a semitone higher.

"We're going to make this business global and we're in talks with a number of potential partners who will allow us to reach new territories quickly."

This did the trick for James, who, sensing better copy from Julian, directed his next few questions to him. We discussed the business plan, model and revenue targets, with me desperately attempting to correct or modify the flagrant exaggerations of Julian's forecasts and pronouncements. I felt like I was a naughty child interrupting a parent on an important telephone call, such was the disdain I discerned in Julian's rigid refusal to look at me directly or qualify positively anything I contributed. James gave no indication of picking up on the tension, or so I hoped. The conversation switched at the end to an enquiry about us and our family backgrounds. James's last question was pretty direct.

"So, you are both fathers. What have you learnt from your own fathers that impacts on your aspirations for the business?" I hadn't seen that one coming. Strangely, Julian's eager and polished reply suggested he knew this was going to be his grand finale. He ran his hand through his fragrant floppy hair and removed his glasses, the tip of which he chewed on for a moment with measured deliberation.

"James, my father went to prison some years ago for insider dealing. He would not mind me telling you, and his experience has shaped my ambition. He was naive and followed others. I know that to really achieve anything in this world, you have to want something so much that it blinkers you from outside distraction and frankly diminishes emotional irrationality and allows you to focus on the right decision, not the decision that feels right. We are going to succeed, because my dad has taught me that being good but weak gets you nowhere."

My mind was filled with conflicting thoughts as James shifted in his chair to face me. Primarily, I was overwhelmed by the nagging suspicion that Julian had learnt that speech in anticipation of the interview and was going to give a version of it irrespective of the question. I was also struggling to put into words the lesson I had learnt from my intellectual and professorial father, who was so disdainful of unchecked entrepreneurialism. Julian had overindulged in dramatic pauses, so I gabbled a confused response.

"A difficult question for me. My grandfather was a great businessman and I really loved learning from him. He had hat shops and as I child I loved being with him to hear how he grew his business. My dad is a professor of political history. He's the enemy of successful business, really, and he would like me to do something dull, like write about the Industrial Revolution in nineteenth-century Germany."

As James was putting away his notebook and recording equipment, I grew uneasy. I knew I should have spoken more favourably about Dad, but I was trying to have the best one-liners. He had told me recently with much excitement about his next book, which had the working title *From the Rhineland to the Ruhr: The Antecedents of Marxist Thinking in German Industrialisation.* It sounded excruciatingly dull, but to Dad it was supremely important. My last hope was that, as an avid *Guardian* reader, he loathed *The Times.* Maybe he wouldn't see it when it came out?

* * *

Later that week, on Saturday morning, I heard the thud of the paper landing through the letter box, and with some trepidation I tiptoed downstairs, picked it up from the mat and, with shaking hands, searched out the article.

For a first profile, it was not a bad one. The colour picture was well framed, and we were smiling, not looking solemn or severe like traditional hard-nosed business magnates. The headline was pretty good too – 'Meet the Parents' – with a subhead that read:

> *PrimaParent is rapidly becoming one of London's most talked about start-ups, with serious backing and ambitions. James Connor meets its two contrasting founders.*

So far so good, and indeed what followed was a very accurate representation of our conversation, with an implicit admiration for the concept and its initial execution. Our concluding remarks about our fathers were reported verbatim. The last paragraph was a summary, which made difficult reading.

> *PrimaParent is an ambitious but credible business proposition, which with luck, tenacity and hard work may one day grow into a significant operation. I was struck, however, by the contrasting and unusual commercial marriage of its parents, Lazarus and Lloyd-Mason. The former is an energetic, enthusiastic, if*

slightly inelegant marketing person, who may create a credible business if he can dial down the jargon and the mantras. Lloyd-Mason is commercial, charming and has an unbending steeliness, which he undoubtedly utilises in any negotiation. They did not pat each other on the back and finish each other's sentences. As parents of this baby business, only time will tell if they have created a sustainable marriage or whether, like so many other aspiring start-ups, even with marriage guidance, it cannot be saved.

I stared out the window at my favourite tree in full bloom in my garden, and contemplated how helpful this article was going to be. After about ten minutes, my phoned pinged. Julian had sent a laconic text: *Why did you contradict me so much?*

10. Family Second

"What were you thinking, Alex? Do you have so little respect for what I do? Important work, which you deride in public."

Sadly, my over-optimism that he would not read *The Times* was shattered about an hour later by a phone call from my incandescent, hurt father, who had been alerted to the article by a well-meaning friend.

"It's not like that, Dad. I was trying to talk about Zeyde's influence on me growing up and perhaps it came out wrong. I wanted to explain where my ambition and drive came from."

"I am not sure what 'right' would have sounded like. And by the way, ambition is not just about commercial success, it is a political aspiration for improvement. You are seduced by the empty noise you generate in the pursuit of recognition. I have to say that, right now, I am not that proud of you, Alex."

"Thanks a bunch. What should I do with that statement? You are not proud of me for building a business or you are not proud of me because I don't share your world view?"

"You know what I feel. The liberation of technology has elevated the pursuit of individual glory above the benefits it brings to the masses."

"Wow, Dad, bit heavy for the weekend. I'm still in my pyjamas, feeding Emily breakfast. Why are you making everything sound so much like a political treatise? My business has just been covered in a national newspaper. Can't you say 'well done'?"

He was momentarily silent. This normally meant that his enormous brain was performing some kind of complicated process of evaluating of whether to engage in an unpleasant argument or retract the confrontational stance in favour of long-term peace. When he resumed the conversation, he sounded much calmer, suggesting that a decision had been made.

"Alex, don't be silly. You know I am always proud of you, no matter how much of a selfish little capitalist you are."

'That's more like my loving father."

"I just need you to try to remember that I raised you on the commune in Finchley to have some more socially aware values."

"Of course, comrade."

"Your grandfather was a great man and built a fine business. But he put nothing back into society around him."

"Maybe, but I am grateful to him for paying my school fees."

"You know I was overruled by your mother. I'd have sent you down the road to the local school without hesitation."

"Convenient that Mum objected and overruled you, isn't it? Best of both worlds. A great education for me without you having to make it happen."

"All right, all right, let's have a truce. It's too tiring. We will see you tomorrow for tea as expected." I didn't think it was a good idea to tell him that I planned to be in the office all day Sunday and was unlikely to make it round.

"Absolutely. Wouldn't miss it."

"Well, judging by your recent commitment to your business, I'm not so sure. With regard to the article, Mum wants you to know that she likes the photo with the story, although why you were dressed as a guitarist from a rock band is beyond us. If only you could look a bit more like your business partner, Hugh Grant."

Before we parted, he suddenly remembered something else he wanted to tell me.

"Oh, by the way, Alex, the *Guardian* is giving me a regular column to write about all things digital. They're keen to get a more radical view on start-up culture. I'm thinking of calling the column 'High Tech or No Tech'."

"Sounds great, Dad. Very cool. Make sure you write nice things about us."

And with that, our spat had ended.

* * *

Life carried on for the first eighteen months of our existence with the frenetic complexity that our desire for success created. It was a really pressurised time in which I felt unable to create a routine that gave me a semblance of normality. Work was one long uncompleted conversation and every time I focused on something elsewhere, I lost its thread and meaning. I have mentioned how little I was around for the kids, but the guilt was less than when I took time out of the office and was not completing a half-started project. When you are not thinking straight about all aspects of your life, you create mitigating arguments in your mind to excuse your behaviour. My false logic derived from the belief that if I was sacrificing a bit of family involvement now, we would all enjoy the benefits of my wealth creation further down the track. I was sure that money would bring choices, which would in turn guarantee greater happiness.

The pressure was unrelenting for everyone. Late one night, a few months after our launch, I was sitting with Dimitri, working on how to make the process of customer registration quicker, when a flustered Alice asked if she could have a chat.

We adjourned to a quiet corner of our busy office. It was nearly 10 p.m. and most of the team were still there. Alice took some deep breaths and tried to calm herself. She appeared slightly manic, a behaviour you would not have expected from her. Normally unflappable, she was definitely flapping a bit now.

'What is it, Alice… you look like you've just run over a kitten?"

"No, that would never happen. I'm a careful cyclist." Something must be up. She normally laughed at my jokes. Staring at some imaginary horizon over my left shoulder, her voice cracked.

"I don't know how you do it?"

"Do what?"

"Put your life on hold to work so ridiculously hard." I wondered where this had come from.

"I'm not sure I know what you mean. We're a young business. We have a lot to do."

She wasn't satisfied with this answer. "When did you last read Theo a bedtime story? When did you last nip out for a quick Indian with Sarah?"

"She hates Indian food."

Alice tutted. "Alex, can you stop being unfunny for a minute and listen to me. I am struggling because this business is ruining my life with Caroline and the kids. Don't get me wrong, I knew we were going to be full on, but this doesn't let up. I feel like I've discovered an ants' nest and am trying to pick up the ants one by one. Don't you question the effort versus the sacrifice?"

For a moment, I felt that I was undergoing a moral examination and, due to a lack of preparation, I would fail. The shallow truth was that I did not empathise with her conflict. I had convinced myself that if you showed any personal weakness, it would undermine your effort at the most crucial point in the company's evolution. It was a binary choice between a balanced life or a successful business. Alice was exhausted by the incredible amount she had achieved in such a short space of time. It was up to me to say something consoling and inspiring.

"Well, at least your kids are guaranteed a great birthday experience this year."

"Really, Alex, is that the best thing you could think of to say to me?" She had a point. I must have been more tired than I thought if that was the most sympathetic response I could muster.

"OK. Take two." I gave her my most winsome smile. It didn't work. She was impervious to what little charm I possessed. "What I meant to say is, of course it's a strain on our family life. Sarah is not happy with me at all." I'm not sure how I had the temerity to suggest this, as I'd been far too busy to actually enquire about her feelings. "It's going to get better, of course it will. Look at what you've built in no time at all. It's a remarkable achievement. You've been the glue in the business. You know the plan. As we grow, the support you'll have will deepen. I guarantee, we will not be having this conversation in a year."

"What if I'm not here in a year?" That threat was a bit unexpected and potentially disastrous. We literally could not find the stapler without Alice. I needed to be convincing in my response.

"Alice. That's bollocks. You are of course going to be here for a long time to come, until the point at which *facelesscorporation.com* pays us millions for our endeavours. As much as I love the sound of my own voice, you love the results of bringing people together to achieve something great. I know you do." It was working, she was listening and relaxing her clenched fists as I went in for the emotional kill.

"So, what we need to do is talk more. I don't want you to store this frustration and internalise your stress. Find me. Shout at me. Kick me in the shins. But share, for God's sake. And why don't you take a long weekend next week to be with Caroline and the kids. We'll still be trading when you come back."

Alice looked at me calmly now, and it was clear that the momentary uncertainty had evaporated. She got up to go.

"Thank you, Alex. You have the bedside manner of an executioner, but you're right. I just need to get through this period until we build a more sustainable operation. I will take you up on the offer of a break. I really need to have a few days off seeing your smug face at such close proximity."

"Excellent. Enjoy some time away." As I said those words and contemplated her brief absence, I started to feel my pulse quicken in panic. "Make sure you have your phone on. Just for emergencies, of course."

* * *

Julian, on the other hand, required very little soothing and was rarely overburdened by guilt for his domestic absence. He was hard-working and committed, but he would occasionally disappear, and in the melee of our crazy and unstructured working, we wouldn't always notice. He always had a gym bag with him and, with my man-crush on his casual handsomeness and toned athleticism, I assumed therefore that he was off releasing those energising hormones associated with vigorous sport that I'd read about. As much as Julian eschewed endorsing the motivational messages I had plastered around the room, he was often teased for his favourite phrase, 'A fit mind and a fit body are one and the same', which he always chanted as he left to go and work out. He seemed to be overcompensating for something.

Our relationship was curious by this stage. We did work well together. He respected my unpredictable brain, which scattered ideas into the wind in the hope that occasionally one would have a chance of being developed. He acknowledged, however, that I was a competent marketer who would sell my grandmother to a pirate for a few more registrations. In turn, I had enormous respect for his shrewd instincts for potential partnerships and his tenacious quest for a good deal on any agreement that came our way – from an employment contract to a photocopier lease. Julian believed every commercial relationship was based on mutual distrust and a desire for exploitation. It was a conflict to be won.

We laughed a lot together at the daily absurdity of our hunt for glory. With sarcasm to PhD level, we could have held a masterclass in answering questions with a facetious quip. We revelled in the crazy people we encountered along the way. Particularly children's entertainers. Often, we'd sit with a glass of wine at the end of the week and have a competition to see who could find the entertainer with the silliest name. Mr Dangle from Wolverhampton was usually the winner.

Julian and I enjoyed each other's company on a superficial level of banter and debate about the business. What we could not muster was intimacy. There was absolutely no discussion about what we did in those rare moments outside the office and he never mentioned his family, which was strange in the context of a business that required some understanding of the rigours of parenting. I would occasionally ask him how Catherine was getting on at work and he would curtly respond 'fine' and move on to another topic.

There was no actual need to share details of our domestic lives and our days were sufficiently busy without the requirement of personal revelation. I was not that surprised when on an ordinary Wednesday morning, as I sat at my desk sipping my first and most crucial coffee, Julian emerged from the lift dragging two enormous suitcases. Silently he moved to the furthest corner of the office and placed them behind some boxes. He motioned for me to join him in The Bored Room. With a furtive glance towards the office, he shut the door and rather formally asked me to sit down.

"Alex, I want you to know that I've left Catherine." He was strangely detached, as if informing me of something mundane like that he had booked a holiday or was moving home.

"I'm so sorry, Julian. Are you OK?" He looked at me with curiosity and clearly thought I had asked him a remarkably irrelevant and patronising question.

"I'm terrific. Why wouldn't I be?"

"Well, call me old-fashioned, but splitting from one's spouse can sometimes be something of a wrench?"

"Not for me, I assure you. I've outgrown Catherine. I'll always be grateful for our time together and we have three lovely children. But Alex, you must have had a sense that she wasn't the one who was going to help me get where I need to."

"In truth, it always seemed to be a bit of a strain when you were together, but it wasn't my place to comment about your relationship. Where will you go?"

'I'm moving in with a friend." His curt delivery clearly conveyed that there was no scope for further conversation about his future whereabouts. I changed tack and asked, with some trepidation, the obvious question.

"What about the children?"

"What about the children? They're little, they're robust. This is unfortunate for them, but not cataclysmic."

"How often will you see them?"

"Really, Alex? How often do you see your kids these days? What's so unusual? I will see them plenty and intend to be the model of a civilised and involved parent as long as Catherine tones down the wailing banshee routine a bit. I would do anything for them. Plus, consider this, *Superdad*. We're hitching our fortune to delivering a parenting solution. Did it not occur to you that understanding single parents would be important too? I'm doing us all a favour by becoming the company expert on the subject."

I didn't want to respond to his last point as it filled me with a tinge of sadness. I am pretty conventional and felt fortunately secure in my marriage to Sarah, to the point that imagining us split-ting up was impossible. Besides, while I knew it wasn't my place to comment, my sympathies were instinctively with Catherine. He had not really shown her much affection or consideration. Julian was sly and clearly wasn't moving in with elderly Mrs Scroggins who ran a boarding house for lonely single men. Maybe he wasn't going to the gym all the time after all?

When I told Sarah later that day, she was a little more forthright in her assessment of the marital decline. "What a total bastard he is. 'I've outgrown Catherine.' Who talks like that about a relation-ship?" I was reticent to commit to an opinion, for fear of giving the wrong one. I knew she equated my business partnership with Julian to his marriage with Catherine. If he was mean to her, it was inev-itable that he would behave the same way to me. As we lay in bed that night, a sleeping baby between us, I actually felt rather secure and able to believe that Julian's transgressions were irrelevant to the state of our business relationship.

Sarah, unaccustomed to me not offering an opinion, looked at me quizzically for a long time. Silence was most unfamiliar. Eventu-ally, I could take the absence of conversation no more and said, "All right, Sarah. I've clearly done something wrong. But if I have, I'm struggling to know what."

"Relax, Alex. I'm pretty confident that Julian managed to have an affair and leave his three babies without any help from you."

"It's very nice of you to say so. I do my best not to wreck homes."

"Well, how do you think you're doing with this home?" She turned towards me and gave me a very specific stare that behoved me to answer the question honestly. As if I would try to spin things. When I spoke, my tone sounded needlessly defensive.

"Fair question, I suppose. I know I'm distracted and not around as much as I'd like, but I'm doing my best to keep the plates spinning."

"The trouble is, a spinning plate, if not constantly turned, eventually smashes. Wow, I'm even beginning to talk in clichés like you." She carried on wistfully. "Alex, I'm so excited that you're trying to achieve what you've always wanted. Really, I am. And of course I'm not going to stop supporting you. But be nice along the way. Julian isn't nice. I just don't want his values to rub off on you in how you treat people."

Julian leaves his wife, and I'm in trouble for bad plate-spinning. It seemed unfair. As I saw it, I was doing everything I could to create future choices. Professional failure terrified me more than personal absence from the family. I'm not proud of this sentiment, but I knew that Sarah was there to prop us all up. The trouble was, I never really checked with her if that was what she wanted to do. I assumed that any ambition Sarah had for her own advancement at work was less important than mine. She saw Julian's unhappy marriage as a sign that those who want to achieve more may also want more in their personal life. This did not apply to me, but my proximity to Julian unsettled her.

The conversation was becoming uncomfortable and the moment anything serious required confronting, I elegantly segued elsewhere. Sensing it might be safe to move on, I rubbed my hands together with exaggerated enthusiasm and asked my beautiful but emotionally neglected wife this impressive question: "Let's speculate a bit. Who do you think he's shacked up with?"

Clearly, Sarah did not feel compelled to answer. She turned her back on me and gathered up the duvet, before switching off her light.

* * *

Family was always the most important thing I could have imagined in my life. Suddenly, however, I had two of them to deal with. There was my real one and there was my business clan. It wasn't that I loved them equally, but I had emotional commitments to both. A growing office of people, sharing the same outlook, generated significant emotional demands that sometimes overtook the everyday needs of relatives, who you inherited rather than recruited.

My sister and I, for example, had always been each other's closest confidants. We were very different personalities bonded by the atavistic need to protect each other. It just so happened that as I started my business, she embarked on the most daunting period of her career. As she became CEO of Better Futures, the Syrian refugee crisis worsened at a truly alarming rate, with over 1.5 million by 2013. She was spending huge amounts of time providing support and protection for children in camps on the Turkish border and was rarely in the country. She ended an embryonic relationship, her first for some time, because she was rigidly focused on saving lives and refused to put her own future ahead of her quest.

My parents worried about her terribly, but it was mingled with enormous pride in her pure desire to alleviate suffering. While they never said it directly, it was not hard to see why they were reluctant to endorse my efforts with the same enthusiasm. I was involved in something without a noble purpose and concurrently was ignoring the important people in my life, who they felt I didn't appreciate. It was the opposite for Judith. She was engaged in something worthwhile, potentially to the detriment of her own personal happiness.

When I look back on all of this, I can see it just made me more driven. I adored my sister, but I could not compete with her altruism. I was going to show those closest to me that I was very impressive and clever. If my parents made little asides about my absence to stir up my guilt, I'm afraid it just made me commit to spending more time in the office, proving to them my own worth.

There was a chance I would not make it into heaven after all.

11. Board Meeting

After eighteen months of eventful trading, buoyed with optimism, I strode purposefully into the office braced for the day ahead. My arrival was announced to everyone several moments before by the mechanical drone of our clunky goods lift, straining the last few inches of its journey with geriatric effort. Bursting with the energy of its fifty-five ambitious employees, the office was nearly full. It was messy and conveyed a sense of chaotic creativity that, while appropriate for a start-up, was rather tiresome if you wanted to find something. I am a stickler for order, which basically made me a conservative old fart in the eyes of my team of millennials when I asked them to tidy up.

I grabbed a coffee from our kitchen, which looked like a student flat after a raucous party. I was practically a barista by now, having used the Gaggia chrome monster we inherited with the space so much. Unlike everyone else, I always cleaned it afterwards, wiping the steam nozzle and shouting to no one in particular: '*Do you want a pastry with that?*'

In The Bored Room, Alice and Simon were putting the finishing touches to a presentation, hunched over a laptop, their mutual disdain clearly visible as they tried to co-operate. Julian had his feet on the table and swivelled from side to side on one of our flimsy, cheap meeting chairs. He was on the phone and he gestured for me to approach as if inviting me into my own meeting room. He finished his call and sat up.

"Are we all set for the board meeting?" he asked cursorily. I resented the implication that I was readying things for him. Simon, ever loyal to his mate, looked up from his typing and quipped, "We will be once Lady Thatcher next to me allows me to do my job."

Alice bristled and clenched her fists to calm her anger. She hated Simon's cavalier disregard, not to mention his blatant sexism. They came to blows regularly and over the last few months I'd had to make sure that they spent as little time together as possible, which was tricky as she was running our operation and managing the budget was a significant part of her responsibilities. Julian subtly supported Simon's disregard for any vestige of appropriate behaviour and continually defended our finance director from censure.

Today was a big day. We were expecting Moshe Shalon and Lord Dobson within the hour. This was the first time we had met in our office, normally using a meeting room in whichever hotel Moshe was staying at that week.

We had a positive story to tell our investors and I wanted to show off the energy in the office. We could ill afford a display of internal rancour among the management team. I whispered discreetly to Alice: "Ignore Simon. He can't talk to you like that. Please let's finalise our presentation in peace. We'll deal with him after."

Julian jumped to his feet, ready for battle, and declaimed: "Children, can we concentrate on the good news. For the next few hours, we need to come across as if we all want to socialise outside the office."

Practical and expedient as ever, Alice snorted with evident irony and continued to type on her laptop.

* * *

We started the meeting punctually.

There had been much amusement and bewilderment from the team outside when the two separate security details arrived in advance to sweep the office. What they were looking for was ambiguous, as there seemed to be no natural vantage points for snipers, and the most lethal weapon in our collective possession was a pizza slicer we used when we ordered late-night takeaway. Even more amusingly, while Moshe's team were always going to be from his home country, it transpired that George Dobson would now only entrust his protection to Israelis too. The office reverberated with the sound of people speaking Hebrew into lapel mikes as our harsh spotlights bounced intermittently off the frames of identical dark glasses.

George and Moshe had hitherto seemed to get on very well. The few times we had been together, they would greet each other with a familiarity that was unexpected and usually they would sit somewhere quietly, talking conspiratorially with their heads so close they almost touched. There was a lot of nodding and it seemed they had a respect for one another that was very real but also intensely private.

Our board included Jane Thomas, one of the investment partners from iSeed. She struggled to have any relationship with either of the other major investors, who seemed to resent her presence at these meetings and would ignore her completely. As a consequence, she was pretty benign to date in her scrutiny. The meetings in those days did not take long. We were expected to give a concise overview of our performance against an agreed plan and to identify funding needs going forward. They seemed to want headlines, not exhaustive detail, and we were happy to minimise the amount of preparatory work we had to do.

Already, in eighteen months we had exceeded my expectations. 200,000 registered to the site and paying a subscription. 2,500 sellers recruited across the country. Revenue of nearly £30,000 a month. We had enough cash in the bank for at least six months and we were about to embark on raising some more investment. Even more miraculously, we were delivering the numbers we had anticipated when we drew up our initial plan.

I was outlining the plan for growth for the next year when Moshe stood up and gestured for me to stop talking. Perhaps more a command with his hand than a gesture, on reflection.

"Guys, I am troubled."

"I'm sorry to hear that," Julian answered. "What's troubling you?"

"Your numbers are wrong."

"I really don't think they are," chipped in Simon with his usual self-belief. I looked at Alice, who subtly nodded in agreement with Moshe.

"Don't make it worse, please," Moshe continued, as if gathering evidence for a future appearance in court. Instinctively, Julian turned to George for approbation but was met with nothing other than the brief statement: "I can't abide sloppiness." Moshe stared back at Simon. Within thirty seconds, what had been a seemingly effortless update on our positive performance started to unravel.

"Where are they wrong?" I ventured. I had long worried about the sloppiness of Simon's work. Numbers seemed not to be his thing, perhaps an Achilles heel for an ambitious finance director. Moshe, who had been assiduously note-taking during our presentation, told Simon to get out of his seat so that he could control the computer, which was being projected on to a large TV screen. Simon reluctantly got up and for the first time since I'd met him, he looked apprehensive. Moshe scrolled straight to a chart with revenue projections. Simon had made a multiplication mistake and clearly this had inflated the final figure.

"Incompetent... Agreed?" We all nodded obediently at Moshe. Simon looked at his feet as if he'd been given a detention.

"There is more." Moshe was just warming up. He found two other figures that were wrong. There was a zero missing on the figure for the hosting of our site. There was also a formula mistake on the final profit chart, which meant that we were making less money than we had presented. The silence that descended was not golden but decidedly awkward. I could not believe that I had missed these mistakes when we reviewed the presentation late the night before. I was not surprised that super-smooth Simon could make such basic errors, but I was angry that I had not called him out for this previously.

Julian spoke first.

"You're right. We'll correct these mistakes and they will not happen again. Now, let's please move on." He was taking this very personally and did not want to engage in further debate. Moshe had the air of someone who was enjoying every minute of the debacle, while pretending to be externally furious. I suspected that he loved these demonstrations of his brilliance and wanted both applause and retribution. He was good, clearly very good, at maths.

"I want an action that will ensure this never happens again," he demanded. Execution not rehabilitation, clearly. No one replied.

"What my learned friend is saying," George Dobson continued, "is that we cannot have our money mismanaged through basic arithmetical mistakes. If you get it wrong on something this simple, how can we entrust you to manage your business when you have rich resources and deeper pockets?"

The message to us was clear, and a sacrifice was required to regain favourable support and patronage. The meeting concluded without incident, but I noticed every time I glanced at Alice that she was smiling.

* * *

"Let's get rid of him now," I shouted. It was a few hours after the meeting had adjourned. Julian had immediately headed out for what turned out to be a boozy lunch with George, as his cheeks were flushed when I confronted him on his return. We were alone among the detritus of coffee cups and biscuits from the meeting in

The Bored Room. I observed that our policy of having children's snacks to reflect our culture needed reviewing. A full plate of Jamie Dodgers and Iced Gems had failed to impress a major tech mogul and a peer of the realm. Julian swivelled on his chair, checking his messages on his phone. He was clearly not going to make the conversation easy.

"Simon has to go. He's useless. He has no attention to detail and is so slapdash. I checked his qualifications properly the other week. He hasn't got any proper ones. I know he's charming, but he's basically rubbish at his job." Julian was petulantly silent. "I don't care if he is your friend and I don't care if you have some establishment code of honour I don't understand. He's a liability."

"Alex. I hear you. I'm just not in the mood to listen to you."

I am a calm person. I have a mindfulness app on my phone. My blood pressure and heart rate are comparable to that of an elite athlete, a chess champion or a nuclear submarine commander. But my taciturn and truculent business partner pushed me to a point of anger that I had not experienced for many years. I don't know how to describe the cloud of fury that enveloped me, but it was certainly transformative.

Not normally one for grand gestures, I began with a theatrical flourish as I swept the papers, biscuits and several cups to the floor. A strangulated scream turned into a simple invocation to Julian to 'put that fucking phone down'. Julian turned in what seemed like slow motion towards me and, in disdainful challenge, elaborately placed the phone next to him.

"Alex, I really do hope that you're going to clear that up."

My anger-turn subsided quickly. I felt slightly ridiculous, which is inevitably a by-product of a loss of control. I was certainly glad that the room itself had thickish walls, so that hopefully my tantrum had gone unnoticed in the open-plan office outside.

"I'm sorry, Julian, but you should engage more respectfully when we have something important to discuss."

He remained unmoved and unrepentant.

"OK, I know Simon has to go. I've noticed the mistakes too," he eventually conceded after moments of spiky silence. "But you are going to fire him and you are going to do it well."

You must surely now have a clear sense that despite our joint billing as founders and CEOs in the business, Julian had a tendency to assume that I was his vassal and inferior subject. It drove me mad as in reality the ideas and vision were all mine, and while he had proved adept at oiling the wheels, he was not really driving the car.

"I will do it now, and I'm going to find a replacement. Alice will keep us going until then. I'm delighted he's not going to get anything."

I had acted on good advice when we set up the business and made sure the shares we had allocated to our three lieutenants were only in the form of options. Simon was going to get 0 per cent of zero. Even he could do that sum. He was contractually due three months' salary and I had no intention of giving him a penny more. The conversation was over. Julian had conceded without ever acknowledging the error of his recommendation. I tidied up the mess a bit while Julian returned to his phone. As I opened the door, I was confronted by an eerily silent office and many pairs of eyes trained in my direction. Perhaps the walls weren't that thick after all?

* * *

Firing people is a test of conscience and character. Whether you are letting someone go due to cost cutting or for reasons of incompetence, you are severing people's livelihood with a disregard for the consequences. Some poor bugger, loyal and hard-working, may just have had a mortgage application accepted predicated on a steady salary, only to find their lives overturned by your need to give them their marching orders.

I had let quite a lot of people go during my time working for others. Most of the time I was instructed when and how to do it by bosses, and I was just the unfortunate messenger stammering through a scripted speech. I hated it, because invariably it was someone in head office telling me to do it and I was watching decent people crumple before me. I never slept the night before a redundancy round as I contemplated the unintended misery that I was about to unleash on innocent families reliant on mum or dad's gainful employment.

Sentiment evaporated when it was my own business and I had felt from the moment we started that we could carry no idle slackers deficient in the necessary skills to make my venture successful. In the case of Simon's dismissal, I felt a frisson of excitement when he joined me an hour later in the now tidy Bored Room. While I was up for a scrap with Simon, he looked resigned to his fate when he sat down and his normal swagger and bravado were absent. The conversation was mercifully short and artificially cordial. Even when a stroppy letter arrived two days later accusing us of breaching several aspects of his contract and me in particular of being a bully, I did not flinch or feel any undue emotion, other than the irritation of having to accept some hefty legal costs to refute his nonsense.

We settled a few weeks later and I had to give him a little bit more money to go away quietly. In the end, it is always better to get a resolution, even if it costs a bit. Argument and disputes can be so detrimental to the focused running of a business. I didn't discuss the negotiation with Julian, nor did he ask me about its progress. And I started to look for a new finance director with the added ingredients of probity and competence.

It was the start, however, of a distance between me and Julian that manifested itself in me making more decisions with Alice and

Dimitri on the operation of the business without always soliciting his sanction. Eighteen months in and we really were doing very well, even if Julian and I were not. We carried on regardless – after all, we were on the cusp of greatness.

12. Serendipity

Starting our business was the hardest thing I had ever experienced. There were so many contrasting pressures to deal with and each very long day had a vagueness to its structure that was not conducive to preserving calm. While we had timings and deadlines to deliver, I sometimes felt that I was triaging crises and problems, unforeseen and unfamiliar, like a naive junior A&E doctor. Digital businesses, moreover, bring with them a barrage of real-time data that supposedly deepens knowledge but can also unleash a compulsion to evaluate performance every five minutes. I soon could not control my urge to check if we had new registrations or sellers, how many people were searching on the site and how long they were spending visiting us. Necessary, of course, to run the business, but an intrusion nevertheless on my regular trips to the loo.

My relentlessness ultimately made my brain ache and my muscles feel weak as I was unable to avert my gaze from the business, which I felt might disintegrate or disappear if I did not worry about its most arcane details. The consequence of this rigid focus was that I felt exhausted all the time. Particularly mid-afternoon, when the caffeine was wearing off, I would often fall asleep at my computer. Once, I awoke to the suppressed muffle of naughty giggles as Julian had taken the opportunity to write 'Ladyboy' on my forehead in red marker.

I took very little time off in that period, working every day, too scared to not be involved in the big decisions and frequently the unnecessary minutiae. I loved the speed and instinctiveness of it all. You liked something or you didn't. There wasn't time for nuanced debate and the spontaneity was liberating.

Our growth increased my appetite for risk. The whole venture was of course risky, but I was now in a world measured by how quickly you went through the cash you had assiduously raised. There is a ridiculous term called 'burn rate' used by start-ups, which measures how quickly you will run out of money as you invest in your growth. We had just over two years from the outset until we predicted we would need some more. Rather than worrying about financial oblivion, I took pride in the speed with which we metaphorically set fire to all that lolly.

It stemmed from the intangible impetus of my evolving ambition. I wanted more all the time: subscribers, sellers, reviews, praise, money and glory. I recognised in myself, as I pursued the growth of the business, an absence of fear or restraint. I saw a distant horizon with any obstacles along the way increasingly out of focus.

* * *

But in the end, it came down to more luck. An enormous serving of it poured from the biggest ladle you can imagine. All the planning, strategy sessions and late-night angst would probably have been for nothing if it hadn't been for a series of events that precipitated the dramatic acceleration of our growth.

It was mid-September and I left the office at 9.30 p.m. on a rainy, squally evening. The moon was a watery sliver in the starless night; it probably wasn't, but let's spice up the narrative. More importantly, on this chilly Wednesday evening Spurs were playing in the cup against Hull and it had gone to penalties after extra time as I slouched towards the Tube station, watching the drama unfold as best I could on Twitter. I couldn't begin the journey home until I knew we had won. As I meandered indecisively, praying for victory, I bumped hard into someone who was clearly moving with pace, causing me to almost drop my iPhone.

"Pay attention, you myopic moron," shouted the dark figure I had shoulder-charged.

I looked up and saw a dishevelled man with an enormous unkempt beard staring at me with contempt and simmering aggression. Rather than going on his way, he squared up, enjoying a clear height-weight-penchant-for-violence advantage. In the event of physical threat I am a bona fide coward, and I immediately went into a submissive and timid state that they don't teach you in self-defence classes. I stammered an apology, noticing at the same time that my voice was unimpressively squeaky.

"I'm so sorry. I hope I didn't hurt you."

"No, but I am thinking that some pugnacious pugilism against someone so pusillanimously puny might placate my pain."

I was a bit confused now. Aggressive and alliteratively verbose at the same time – an unusual combination. I must have grown brave, as I drew back and stared at him with surprise, and he seemed to calm down as his eyes focused on me with puzzlement. Suddenly he emitted a stagey baritone laugh, which defused any threat of being beaten up.

"By the Helmet of Odin! It's little Alex Lazarus."

I was confused, because I could not make out his face beneath a beard so wild it probably had its own ecosystem.

"I'm sorry, do we know each other?"

"Oh Alex, how cruel can you be? It is I, your erstwhile companion through the vicissitudes of scholastic learning. You will remember, I believe, my long-forgotten moniker, Nigel O'Connor."

"My word, it's you, Nigel. I can't believe I didn't recognise you."

"Well, Alex, you were always slightly backward. It's why I took pity on you. I must say, though, you are a tonic for my misery tonight. Your Hebrew God has brought us together for a reason."

"What is that?" I asked, struggling to work out what he was saying through the affectation.

"We must imbibe some alcohol together immediately. Let's walk back to Shoreditch House. They revere me there."

He hooked his arm through mine and dragged me back from whence I had come, to join him in what was clearly not his first drink of the night. Who was I to argue? After all, Nigel O'Connor, better known under his writing pseudonym of Clyde Pilestone, was arguably one of the most successful commercial writers in the world.

* * *

Nigel sat next to me at school when we were thirteen and for several years thereafter. We were not close friends, but we did spend a lot of time together. This was out of necessity, because I was invariably lending him my homework to copy as he had very little interest in doing any himself. He was what you would now call an outlier in our academic community, indifferent to the niceties of pupil obedience and fuelled by sardonic disdain for the rules of the classroom in which he was forced to sit on a daily basis.

He was extremely clever, though. While structured exam-oriented learning seemed beneath him, he excelled at English, Latin and Greek. At our school we had an enigmatic classics teacher, Dr Taylor. We knew little about him, other than that his first name was Hector and he was supposedly a Soviet spy, recruited at Cambridge in the 1950s. Nigel was his acolyte and trotted after him most break-times, hanging on to his faded and tatty academic gown and discussing some obscure classical text.

When not lost in Virgil, Nigel was creating mischief. He would cultivate friendships with vulnerable individuals, but just as they felt secure in the sunshine of his charismatic personality, he would drop them with casual indifference. Teachers showing any weakness would be tortured with sadistic glee. A chemistry teacher, Mr Watts, was reduced to tears one afternoon by Nigel's refusal to stop asking questions about the difference between *sodium* and a *sodomite*.

I got on with Nigel as well as was possible with an adolescent sociopath. He persuaded me to open my exercise books continually to allow him to ignore the 'bourgeois preoccupation with rote learning' (not a phrase you forget) and we would occasionally hang around together out of school. At fourteen, he was obsessed with dragging me to obscure films with an '18' certificate that were controversial or shocking. I spent many a school holiday sitting in empty cinemas watching classics like *A Clockwork Orange* and *Last Tango in Paris*, wishing I wasn't there.

By the time we started our A levels, Nigel and I had far less to do with each other. We had a different timetable and I felt no need to cultivate a friendship with someone so toxic. Nigel did not last long at the school. He had become the main source of recreational drugs for quite an extensive network of academic institutions. Unfortunately, his trafficking labyrinth got too extensive and he was rumbled by a lethal coalition of an angry parent, our headmaster and a large contingent of local police. After his expulsion, we never met again, and it was something of a relief.

Nigel's transformation into a global publishing phenomenon seemed unlikely after spending his twenties travelling the world, shrouded in a smoky haze of substance experimentation and dissolute behaviour that would have made Lord Byron blush. His lost years contributed to his allure and the exotic danger he craved made him a more compelling literary figure, but in reality, his image was carefully cultivated by adroit publishers with an eye for a strong marketing narrative.

After a nomadic decade, Nigel decided to return home and seek fame with, ideally, a bit of fortune thrown in. He knew he was a good storyteller – indeed, he had beguiled many unsuspecting

women into relationships with apocryphal tales of his swashbuck-
ling adventures at the hands of Somali pirates, Congolese warlords
or any other impressive-sounding enemies. His love of classical literature allowed him to cultivate the persona of a heroic poet complete
with flowing locks and fast fists for bar-room brawls. But he was
also, despite the artifice, very savvy about tastes and commercial
appeal and decided that the teen literary world was ready for a
contemporary new sci-fi universe written with the kind of sarcastic
humour a teenager would love. Working in a bar at night, he sat
down to write in the day. Nigel O'Connor, carousing dilettante,
became Clyde Pilestone, author of the 'Resilient Martian' series.

I suppose I don't really need to go into enormous detail about
the books, as there can only be hermetic monks and Albanians who
have not read the novels or seen the films. The story of Xargon 5,
the time-travelling survivor of the Galaxy Correction Fleet war
on Mars searching the universe for fellow Martians who have also
survived the attack, captured the post-digital consciousness of teens
and parents alike. The sardonic wit and the incorporation of futuristic social media channels into the stories created a frenzied and
unflinchingly loyal fan base.

His tenacity in finding a publisher was unwavering. Rejected
consistently and aware that he could not get his manuscript through
the gatekeeper's gatekeeper's gatekeeper, he decided on direct action.
Over a year-long period, Nigel found casual work at three publishers and two major literary agencies. Under the cover of working
late, Nigel identified and targeted key editorial directors and agents,
leaving a manuscript with a handwritten scrawl on the front page,
as if from an imaginary colleague. Comments like '*Wow, you must
read this*', '*Best thing I've read in years*', '*I think we may have found
our golden goose*'. In most cases, the ploy was rumbled when people
noticed identical manuscripts on more than one desk.

It only needed one person to fall for Nigel's artifice. Kate Williams was a frustrated young agent ground down by chauvinistic colleagues and formulaic commercial demands for new material. She was desperate for a discovery to announce her as a major force in literary London. When she found the dog-eared copy of the manuscript with the barely legible scrawl '*Love this more than my children. Must act immediately!*', she started to hyperventilate, and committed to devoting her energies to introducing Martians to a global audience.

She secured a ridiculous first-time publishing deal, devoting limitless energy to promotion. The experience of bringing his book to life created an active disdain in Nigel for the publishing industry and an indifference to his loyal and obsessive agent. The commercial demands of his success were to be endured rather than celebrated. He was a genius and they were vassals charged with making him look better. It was bad enough to have been born with the name Nigel. To be saddled with the enigmatic pseudonym of Clyde Pilestone ('sounds like a cowboy porn star,' he lamented) to make his books sell better was an insult he would never forgive. The pain of his ascent would be rectified by the subsequent unreasonableness of his behaviour.

Four books, three films and hundreds of merchandising millions later, Nigel bumped into me on the street. Lubricated by an afternoon's solitary drinking and restless for revenge on the intellectual pygmies who had made his life so difficult, he was ready to do something drastic. How lucky for me.

* * *

I had never been so close to a global superstar and had no inkling of what it was like to have to contend with the adulation, deference and staring. At Shoreditch House, beautiful staff ushered us to a discreet corner table and brought a bottle of single malt, two tumblers and an ice bucket, without us even placing an order. While it was dark in our corner, Nigel's distinct hipster-meets-trampy-Viking look made him easily recognisable. I was aware of drinkers pretending not to gawp, while staring intently in our direction and whispering to each other excitedly. How difficult it must be to live with such fame and adulation constantly, and Nigel seemed to be sedating himself with drink to blur the intrusion of others.

We clinked glasses and sat in momentary silence. I had the sense that Nigel was waiting for a cue to address me, but I wasn't sure how to initiate the conversation. Eventually he leant forward and grabbed my hand in drunken camaraderie, asking: "Alex, it has been a lifetime since we spoke. Precis the intervening years for me without losing my interest."

It sounded like an English exam question from a teacher with a short attention span. As you know, I prefer either a florid speech or a pithy summary, so I started to sift throughthe relevant fragments of memory to do justice to my fascinating life story.

"Well, I think the last time we saw each other you were being dragged away in a police van."

"Ah yes," he reflected wistfully. 'My drugs empire cruelly dismantled by the repressive authorities."

"Nigel, you were selling drugs to fourteen-year-olds in swimming pool changing rooms. You were hardly Scarface. Anyway, where to begin? I went to university and read history." He immediately looked bored, so I decided to speed up my life story a little.

"Worked in advertising for fifteen or so years. Married to a GP. Two children." Nigel gave a large theatrical yawn. Emboldened by his evident disdain, I thought there was no point mentioning any other biographical detail that would make me more mundane in his eyes. Sod him, I was going to proclaim my greatness.

"This year, I launched what will become the most successful parenting website in the world and will make me so much richer than you, writing those silly books of yours. PrimaParent is only a few months old, but we are being talked about as the next digital unicorn." (How's that for bravura?) He considered the statement for a second and his expression changed to one of contemplation. Maybe I wasn't such a suburban dullard after all?

"You have some spirit, Lazarus. I was worried you had sunk to a level of ordinariness that exceeded the mediocrity you showed at school." I had read in articles about him that he had few friends and was something of a loner, and now I understood why.

"Nigel, your feedback means the world to me, but let's talk about you. What are you writing now?" I was desperate to change the subject and suddenly longing for my bed. He was exhausting, like an overtired toddler.

"I have just completed the fifth and best book in the series. I am surprised you have not been following the dispute I am having with my publisher." He seemed offended. Actually, I vaguely recalled that I had read he'd gone on a 'writer's strike' because he didn't want to kowtow to his contractual requirements.

"But if you're in a dispute with your publisher, when and how is the book going to appear?"

"I have so much money I make Croesus look like a pauper, and therefore I can employ the most aggressive lawyer imaginable to get me out of my onerous contract. I most definitely will not be in thrall to these people who have bought second homes and garish boats as a consequence of the brilliance of my creative muse."

"So how are you going to get the next one published then?"

"That, indeed, is the sixty-four billion dollar question. I have publishing vultures hovering overhead waiting to swoop down and gobble up the entrails of my last contract. I am being courted by the literati of London to win my favour and the faux adoration is quite frankly demeaning."

A little thought wormed into my head. It was so ridiculous that it could not be adequately described as 'chutzpah'. It was way beyond that. I heard Julian's voice in endless meetings state that our success would evolve from becoming a proper content hub.

"I tell you what, Nigel," I proclaimed with a flourish. "Why don't you let my amazing site publish your next book? We are all about giving parents the chance to do amazing things for their kids. What could they do that's better than giving them an exclusive chance to read the next 'Resilient Martian' book?"

"Alex, I appreciate that you want to make an impression, but you are elevating yourself way above your natural little station in life. You are tiny Alex Lazarus. Husband to a GP and father to ordinary children. You are a follower. You couldn't inspire. Why would I want to be associated with you?"

By now I was oblivious to how rude he was. It was late at night and I was in no rush to go home. Somehow I had managed to remember to text Sarah as we sat down, with the cryptic message: *Am going for drink with Clyde Pilestone. Will explain.* She had immediately replied: *Don't rush back, am in bed with Idris Elba.* I realised I would have a job to do to convince everyone, but at that moment, it was time to rise to the challenge that Nigel had issued.

This was yet another pitch, but possibly the most important one I had made to date. Calmly, I very quickly outlined the vision for the business and why we believed we would become not just a marketplace but also a natural home for entertainment brands. Nigel actually forgot his affectation and asked some perceptive questions, which I did not expect.

After perhaps twenty minutes, I could see that it was time to reach a conclusion as the booze was beginning to defeat him and he struggled to stifle a series of expansive yawns. I had once been told that if you were ever in danger of losing an audience, make an unexpected noise to refocus their energy. I saw Nigel sinking into sleep's willing embrace and I panicked. Should I clap my hands or just yell 'Wake up, sleepyhead'? In the end, hedging my bets, I did a bit of everything and made a strange noise that was a cross between a yodel and a football chant.

I stood up and confidently made this promise while leaning over him: "I guarantee you one thing if you let me publish your book on PrimaParent"

"What's that, my child?"

"You will piss off the entire publishing and literary world and make a lot of people very angry."

Nigel O'Connor aka Cylde Pilestone leapt up and embraced me. My nose was forced into the crook of his arm and I was engulfed by a noxious combination of stale smoke and sour alcohol. Not answering my question, he simply chose to recite some poetry:

"Bliss was it in that dawn to be alive / But to be young was very heaven!"

"Very nice quote. But does that mean we have a deal?"

"It's Wordsworth, you fool, describing the French Revolution. We are about to cause mayhem and dismantle the establishment. So, you bet we have a deal, my little friend. My expensive lawyers will contact your cheap grubby ones tomorrow. Rancour will be rife, and the riled will request revenge. Now let's drink together properly."

He raised his hand and out of the darkness a waitress appeared. And I knew I was in for a long night.

"Champagne, Celestial Maiden! The world is about to think I am even more bonkers than usual."

13. Acceleration

"Clyde Pilestone is letting us publish his next novel. Of course he is. And I got a text from Mozart asking if we could stream his latest opera." Julian folded his arms contemptuously. My attempt to explain what had happened the night before was not going too well.

"First Sarah and then you. Why won't anyone believe me?" I had dragged myself to work early with an enormous hangover to grab a coffee with him. Hangovers were fairly unfamiliar, but Nigel had insisted that I carouse with him until 3 a.m., although I tried to pace myself by sipping timidly and watering an adjacent plant when Nigel wasn't looking.

"Alex, you cannot be telling the truth. Did you misunderstand your conversation with him? Perhaps he just said that he was happy to give you a signed copy of his next book?"

"I appreciate this is a bit unexpected, but I promise you that it both happened and is agreed. Look, he's weirder than Dimitri, but I appealed to his rebellious nature and he basically wants to create publishing mayhem. I know it won't be easy to finalise everything, but we may just have become the luckiest start-up in Shoreditch."

Julian looked at me sourly. I wasn't expecting him to eulogise my brilliance, but I had hoped he'd show a bit more enthusiasm than he was currently mustering. When I went through the minutiae of the conversation as best I could recall, he nodded a lot and was clearly convinced that I was not fantasising. His praise was circumspect.

"Well done, old chap. But the devil will be in the details that I have to negotiate with his lawyers, who I am sure, unlike their client, will be totally sober." It was odd how he had appropriated the responsibility so quickly. Fortunately, before I said something really combative, we were joined by Alice and Dimitri, who had intuited that we were clearly having a significant conversation and did not want to be excluded.

"What are you two egomaniacs arguing about this time?" Alice asked chirpily, spot on in her character assessment. The excitement of the opportunity had become enmeshed in our budding rivalry. Even Dimitri, a man with the emotional intelligence of a man without emotional intelligence, sensed tension.

"Alex. Julian. Tell us what the problem is. It had better be big to take me away from proper work."

Julian smiled and ran his hand through his shiny floppy hair, which I had come to realise was his way of drawing attention to what he was about to say.

"All is good. We have some very exciting news to tell you about an unexpected development we've been working on." I'm not sure he could have irritated me more at that moment if he'd produced a feather duster and tickled me in the face. I resented his doubt that I could bring in something so significant to the business and I especially resented his subsequent appropriation of the success. Making it even worse, he turned to me and said, "Alex, why don't you tell them our news?"

I gritted my teeth and decided, for the time being, to be the nobler man. Jumping to my feet with the irritating perkiness of a children's TV presenter, I asked: "Who likes the 'Resilient Martian' series of books?"

To my surprise, Dimitri smiled broadly. "I love them. First book I read in English."

Alice was more circumspect. "Not really my bag. Working with you lot is enough of an unreal world of adventure for me. But I know lots of normal people who love them. Why do you ask?"

"Because we are going to have the exclusive rights to publish the next one."

"Of course we are. And I've been asked to star in the next James Bond film." Dimitri made himself chuckle with that one.

Alice didn't want to be left out of the banter. "Don't mock, everyone. If he says that one of the most successful writers in the world wants to give our little operation the chance to publish his book, who am I to disbelieve him."

Julian was smirking, as Alex-baiting was his favourite sport. I told the story again in a precise and unemotional rendition, minimising the triumphalism and concentrating on the enormity of the opportunity. When I reached a natural conclusion there was the silence of disbelief, coupled with the realisation that today was pivotal for all of our futures. Julian took charge.

"Not so inept, is he?"

Dimitri grimaced and started to drum the table with his fingers, which I had come to recognise as a sign of fear. "How are we going to cope with demand? It will be like an invasion. You never told me I was going to have to build something that could cope with this. Of course, you are all not smart enough to have thought this through."

Alice was also succumbing to mounting panic. "I mean, of course it's a good thing, but it's also a bad thing. Don't get me wrong, Alex – wow, how did you pull this off? But we could drown. We could become the target of lunatic fans who are disappointed if something goes wrong. This could be too big an opportunity." She trailed off, losing herself in distracted fear and catastrophising.

Sensing the need for leadership, if not a killer speech, I said, "Right, chaps. This is huge. We are ambitious. We are simply going to make it work, starting now," and I got up and walked out of the meeting room. When I arrived at my computer and sat down, I glanced back to see if everyone had followed me, but they were clearly rooted to the spot in fear. After a couple of minutes, I began to suspect that my grand gesture had not worked as hoped, so I sheepishly popped my head round the door to see Julian standing, pen in hand, by the flip chart, orchestrating an animated discussion.

"Oh, we thought you couldn't handle the pressure, so we started without you."

* * *

I called Nigel the next day to confirm that I had not dreamt the whole thing, which of course would have been supremely embarrassing after assiduously overcoming the collective doubt of my colleagues. To my pleasant surprise, he had actually taken decisive action himself and informed his lawyers to take our call and not question his decision. He concluded with an arcane phrase: "This will be a Sisyphean task for you, Alex, but I want it to happen."

I thanked him and, after hanging up, quickly looked up the myth of Sisyphus, the ancient king condemned to push a huge rock up a steep hill, only for it to keep rolling back. I was going to have to mug up on Greek myth if I was to stay interesting to Nigel.

Later that day, we got a call from his lawyer and his agent, Kate Williams. She was polite, but most definitely bemused by the events that had unfolded. There was a clear danger of her being made to look an epic fool rather than a classical hero if this went wrong. Julian and I met her the following day to tell her about our business. With a look of pain and despair, she politely heard our sales pitch, which suggested our aim had always been to become a publishing hub for global blockbusters. She made no attempt to hide her feelings as she put her head in her hands and groaned. We knew she was being theatrical to make a point, but we still felt pretty silly sitting there waiting for her to say something nice, which seemed increasingly unlikely.

"Gentlemen, and I say this with enormous respect and even a bit of admiration: you are both, without doubt, the biggest chancers I have met in some time. The level of your ambition is only, it seems, matched by the scale of your bullshit. The temerity you have displayed in persuading my client to do something reckless with his literary future is so staggering that it might just overcome and kill me. This is the most ludicrous idea Nigel has ever had, and I suppose, Alex, you should be applauded for the surgical precision with which you have identified his suicidal recklessness in tackling the literary establishment."

She was flushed by now with either anger or despair, probably both. Julian, undeterred, smiled at her unctuously and said, "So, where do we sign?" Kate looked momentarily like she wanted to assault him with the heavy clay teapot on the meeting room table, but then dissolved into helpless and slightly manic laughter.

"That pretentious twat will be the death of me. He is completely unhinged and spoiling for a fight at any hour. Even if I proved to him that you both had a criminal record for kidnapping children or were morris dancers in your spare time, I don't think I could dissuade him from an idea once he has committed. Let's ignore the fact that this is the worst idea imaginable and pretend you know what you're doing."

"Kate, you can trust us," said Julian, with all the sincerity of a carpet salesman.

"Julian, I assure you I never will, but we will make do. Now, let me tell you how the book is coming on. I suppose he didn't mention that it isn't quite finished yet?"

"Actually, he gave me the impression that it was ready to upload to our site tomorrow. Must have been the sixth Calvados that made his thinking a little fuzzy."

"No, this one has been a bit more problematic for him and he's secretly nervous about its reception. I suspect that's why he's happy to bury it on an obscure website. No offence, lads."

"None taken. How long have we got?" Secretly, I was very relieved.

"You probably have nine months, give or take. But don't underestimate how much there is to do. I haven't quite got him out of his current deal, and we haven't even broached the subject of how we make some money when this book comes out. The way I see it, you're going to get a lot of traffic to your site, which is going to raise its value significantly. I'll be damned if I'm going to give you anything more than that."

"You drive a hard bargain, Kate." Julian flashed his most alluring smile, which I had seen him do many times. I'm sure he wasn't flirting, but he had the arrogance of a very handsome man whose success was buoyed by his self-belief.

"Of course I do. I have to protect Nigel's interests. After all, we're getting married in three months." Smiling, as an afterthought she raised her left hand to prove the point and flashed a shiny platinum ring with a lustrous, twinkling diamond the size of a golf ball.

* * *

The next few weeks were frenzied mayhem. There was no margin for error in any of our decisions and I told myself that everything needed to be sacrificed in the pursuit of this opportunity. It made me unreasonable in the office and not much better when I was at home. Sarah told me one evening, when I could hardly speak through a combination of exhaustion and overwhelming fear, that our family life was 'running on fumes'. We didn't speak too much more about it, but I made a commitment that I would stop by the garage for a top-up, just as soon as I could see straight.

Julian spent an inordinate amount of time with Kate and an enormous team of lawyers, accountants and representatives of the different interested parties in the work of Clyde Pilestone. I joined him for some meetings but trusted him to secure a deal that would allow us maximum benefit from this unusual partnership. Our presence was met with incredulity as they watched the money machine being dismantled needlessly by its author. Julian relished their resentment. Safe in the knowledge that we were untouchable because of Nigel's patronage, he used a combination of arrogance and unreasonableness as his principal negotiating technique.

Nigel only wanted to deal with me and had no interest in meeting my business partner, much to the annoyance of Julian, who felt that I was controlling the relationship to exclude him from participating properly. I was sandwiched between two contrasting views – Nigel, who demanded that whenever we met it was just us, after 10 p.m. and underpinned by steady late-night drinking, my worst nightmare, and Julian, whose admonishments to be included were incessant and angry.

"Alex, how on earth can I negotiate properly unless I can have a relationship with him? Be the bigger man and allow me to participate. Stop worrying about me stealing your precious school friend." I tried to tell him it wasn't my decision, but he didn't believe me. In the end, there was a brief meeting at Kate's offices when Nigel stopped by to take his fiancée out for lunch. He was a different person in front of her, and the pretension was replaced by someone softer. Julian was surprised by the down-to-earth and meek individual who was not the cavalier iconoclast I had painstakingly described. What I now realised underpinned Nigel's many complex personas was a fear of failure and sensitivity to criticism. He was terrified his latest book would be an abject failure and he would be jettisoned from public affection. He had struggled to write this last instalment and was reluctant to let it out before it had undergone meticulous and paranoid revisions.

There was a logic to the madness of giving us this publishing exclusive. The core theme of the book was the depletion of the universe's mineral reserves through the folly of its civilisations as the earth quite literally crumbled beneath the feet of our hero. Nigel had realised that there was something satisfyingly apposite in removing the destruction of trees from the book's publication. It was therefore only to be available as a digital download from our site, readable on a variety of standard e-readers.

As the weeks wore on, we did reach a mutually beneficial agreement with Kate. We would enjoy an enormous increase in subscriptions and would keep the massive hike in fees that would generate. The download revenue would ostensibly go to Nigel. If sales globally reached certain levels, we would get tiered bonuses. Julian adroitly negotiated that we would also get rights to the next book. It was quite frankly unprecedented and shrouded in rigorous confidentiality agreements, which afforded us some protection to prepare for launch without the global scrutiny. Kate's tenacity at unpicking these publishing agreements without subsequent litigation was impressive and intimidating.

Meanwhile, back at our HQ, the frenetic activity was akin to the Allied preparation for the D-Day landings. Dimitri was dealing with the challenge of the world suddenly coming to our site all at once. This required a massive increase in servers and infrastructure, and he embarked on a quest to beef up our operation to handle the demand. He was in his element and like a military commander barking orders at an ever-expanding army of foot soldiers. We left him to get on with whatever he needed to do and turned a blind eye to the fact that reports kept surfacing that Supreme Leader Kharkachov was keeping himself sane through a series of successive relationships with colleagues who somehow found his enigmatic genius enticing. While proximity and hard work were the catalysts for many an office tryst, Dimitri was oblivious to the danger and inappropriateness. Alice pushed me to intercede and make him aware of the perils of his office-centred libido.

"He is a lawsuit or grievance claim waiting to happen," she bemoaned. "Please do something."

"I will, I promise." I had no such intention as we were so out of our depth, and I was reluctant to risk upsetting this mercurial if uncontrollable force so crucial to future success.

We needed to recruit like crazy and continually look at how we were structured. The core business was doing well; we were bringing in new sellers steadily and the number of subscriptions was on plan. But we realised we needed to be much bigger before we embarked on our imminent adventure, so we had to beef up our sales and customer service teams. More importantly, we also had to bring in people who understood the world of publishing and entertainment. Oh yes, and we had to think about building an international presence pretty quickly.

Kate had insisted that we have a robust office in the US or, in her words, 'I will withdraw all conjugal affection from Nigel until he decides to publish with grown-ups.' To prevent her dismantling the tracks of our future gravy train, I acted quickly. We luckily had a bright graduate marketing exec, Jamie, with both a UK and US passport, making her the automatic (and only) choice for our New York office. She and I nipped out there to find some premises, and within a couple of weeks she was packing her bags and jettisoning a distraught boyfriend to become general manager of our first overseas office. She couldn't believe our desperation.

By the end of our second year of trading, we were a very fast-growing business with one hundred and twenty staff crammed into an overflowing office in London and a team of five completely out-of-their-depth youngsters in New York. In six months, we were going to be publishing *The Galaxy Slayer's Last Stand*, the fifth 'Resilient Martian' novel, which was going to cause a sensation. There was only one slight snag.

We were running out of money.

14. Cap in Hand

As soon as we signed the deal to publish Clyde Pilestone, we knew we needed to fund massive expansion. The nature of our agreement was predicated on a global footprint that we didn't have. Time for the sun to rise on our empire.

George Dobson and Moshe had reacted quite differently. The former, indifferent to teen literature, was ambivalent to our coup and failed to grasp the enormity of our success. In a series of curt emails, he suggested forcibly that this was not where he thought we should be focusing our efforts. He also made it clear there was likely to be no more money forthcoming. Julian was unbothered and told me that George was distracted by business interests in China, so had little energy to divert elsewhere.

Fortunately, Moshe had already called by the time I received George Dobson's last email, hyperventilating down the phone with excitement.

"Alex... Alex. What have you done? How is this possible? You are a little boy. Could it be you have become a man?"

"Moshe. You are the first person to believe I could persuade someone famous to do a deal with us."

"I didn't believe you could do this. No way. But when Julian rang, he managed to persuade me you weren't a complete fool."

"What do you think now?"

"I think it is time for me to increase my investment in your business. You need to do a lot very quickly. And I want you to make sure that this time, I get more than Dobson."

"You needn't worry. He seems to respect me even less than you and thinks we're wasting his time. But we are going to need a lot more money, unless you want to fund our entire international expansion."

"I have an idea for that, little boy."

"Please stop calling me that, Moshe." He seemed unable to have a positive conversation without the need to assert his mastery by always unsettling me. It was not intimidating, simply very irritating. "So, what is your idea, or am I too young to understand your wisdom?"

"There is no need to be rude to a major investor. That does not impress me, *habibi*." He accentuated the colloquial Arab term for 'darling' with a sneer and a long silence in which he expected me to apologise, genuflect or weep with shame. I felt required to break first and acknowledge some gratitude for his financial generosity.

"OK, Moshe, I'm sorry. I won't be disrespectful to you any more, even if you can't return the compliment. What's your great idea?"

He was smug in victory. "You are going to go over with Julian to meet Cole and Brooke Johnson and they are going to give you the Series A funding you need. I'll top up too, if they come on board."

"Wow. I've always wanted to meet them, they're fascinating. But I've read they no longer invest in start-ups?"

"You must not believe the PR statements of super-successful people. We like to control the narrative. Surely you have realised that by now?"

"Why would they want to see a little boy like me, Moshe?'

"Because I have just called them and told them to meet you in forty-eight hours. You had better ask your mummy if you can go on a small trip."

He had the last word, and inevitably it was a put-down.

* * *

Cole and Brooke Johnson were the supreme power couple of Silicon Valley and their home in Woodside, five minutes out of town, was the most spectacular house I had ever visited. Cradled in a forest clearing, surrounded by lush vegetation and a resplendent rose garden, it was a curious architectural melange – part Pablo Escobar Hacienda, part Palace of Versailles. Julian and I were shown by a maid into a vast living room with a floor-to-ceiling window running the length of one side, overlooking an infinity pool the size of a lake. The sofas were truly enormous and despite, neither of us being particularly short, we struggled to lean back and touch the floor with our feet at the same time.

"Do you think this thing is intended to intimidate us?" Julian bemoaned.

"Maybe we've climbed the beanstalk and now we have to beg the giant for gold?" For good measure, I started intoning, 'Fee-fi-fo-fum, no more funding for this English—"

We were interrupted by an enormous sliding door opening and the emergence of our hosts. There was an iridescent gleam as the sunlight fell on the immaculate straight white teeth of Brooke, whose face was stretched into an enormous, flawless smile. She strode towards us, arms outstretched, with forceful confidence.

"You must be Alex and Julian. Welcome to *Àu bout de souffle*." She shook both of our hands with vigorous enthusiasm.

"Lovely to meet you," Julian replied, holding her gaze with equal, if slightly uncalled for, intensity. "It's a strange name for a house so magnificent, I have to say."

Brooke laughed with a manly baritone depth. "It's French, as you know, for 'breathless'. I think if you are truly ambitious, you should be out of breath most of the time. Don't you?"

As they continued their flirtatious staring at one another, I was aware of another presence in the room. Her husband, Cole, had shuffled in quietly and was observing us with a look of curious detachment.

Cole is a muscular American name suggestive of a tall, powerful sporting frame with the debonair looks of a movie star. Not this Cole, however. He could at best be described as squat and scruffy, and while his wife was immaculately dressed and radiating health, he had a pockmarked face and a straggly reddish beard. His creased tee shirt was emblazoned with the memorable phrase 'Cocaine Made Me Rich', and it looked, as he did, completely unwashed.

"Hey, guys," he whispered nonchalantly. "What brings you to our little cottage in the woods?"

"Money," ventured Julian boldly. "We need lots of it."

"Well, we have plenty of the stuff." He flopped down into the sofa next to his now seated wife. She completed the sentence. "We are just very fussy who we give it to."

* * *

Cole and Brooke were an oddity in Silicon Valley. You'd expect grungy Cole, from the picture I have just described, to be a maths genius who built computers in his garage as a teenager, like his idol Bill Gates, while football jocks slammed his head into the wall at high school and girls shunned him. Actually, Brooke turned out to be the glamorous face of coding. She built a revolutionary publishing software tool, eventually bought by Microsoft, while also being known as something of a party animal. By the time she was twenty-five she was worth $10m, and it was in an LA nightclub that she met out-of-work actor Cole Johnson. Their tumultuous love affair became the most robust business partnership imaginable.

Cole was not much of an actor, with neither the looks for the romantic lead nor the versatility to carry off quirky characterisation. He did a bit of theatre and TV, but to little acclaim, and once played

Macbeth so badly that his only review described his acting as 'more tragic than the play itself'. What ensured his future salvation was his fascination with technology and the commercial opportunities it offered.

In Brooke, he realised that he had not simply triumphed finding a beautiful girlfriend; her fearsome ability to write software was going to be much more lucrative than snagging the part of 'tubby dad' in a laxative commercial. Very quickly they moved into an apartment overlooking the Golden Gate Bridge and an office in Menlo Park, where they built 'Can-Act Software' (Cole's little joke). Several years later, it was sold for over a billion dollars, having revolutionised the basic finance packages available to small companies across the world. Everyone knew the story, but not the truth behind their success.

As the business flourished, their marriage floundered. Passion dissolved into rancour and disdain. It was quite a dilemma – personal incompatibility versus their collective professional dynamism. Cole was an instinctive CEO and Brooke a software genius with a single-minded relentless focus on product development. They couldn't stand each other's company, and behind closed doors co-existed in glacial indifference to one another. Yet they realised that their personas and perceived marital harmony were very good for business. The beautiful geek in love with the energetic performer added a lustre to their business that could be manipulated to great effect. There was no way that their boundless ambition was going to be scuppered by the shortcomings of their marriage.

So, they agreed to present the image of an engaging couple seen out everywhere together, hand in hand, seemingly inseparable. Once home in their secluded mansion, they lived completely apart, visited by friends, families and lovers, who were entertained in discrete wings of the property. I found this out from Moshe, who somehow knew Brooke well. Before our departure, he confided that their marriage was 'less real than the tooth fairy'. They were a business partnership, not a family. In an interview in the *Wall Street Journal*, Brooke admitted: 'I can't have children. It's not gynecological. It's just I would lose my edge.' They approached potential deals without sentimentality and were implacably sceptical of most start-up promises. Yet it was worth the pain, as their ability to spot the success was legendary.

Given their marital facade, they approached investment as an indivisible team made up of contrasting and complementary skills. If the Johnsons invested in your business, you got both of them on your board as a non-negotiable precondition. Brooke would scrutinise your technology platform and Cole would terrorise your marketing and sales team. They wrote a book together called *What the Board Can Learn from a Happy Marriage*, and their PR machine ensured that they were always interviewed as a double act, doling out wisdom harmoniously.

"They are going to mess with your head," Moshe had gleefully concluded. "Brooke will flirt with you to test you. Well, not you, Alex, but I am sure she will like Julian. Good luck."

* * *

If you knew the status of their relationship, the nuances of their behaviour towards each other were not hard to pick up on. The conversation was cordial, and although they did not contradict each other, nor did they particularly interact. Brooke maintained an intense, almost uncomfortable focus on Julian, oblivious of my flimsy presence. She twirled her shiny blonde hair distractedly in her fingers, but there was something calculating in the mannerism. To make the atmosphere stranger, Cole sat next to me at a slight angle, so close to my face that I could not only smell his breath but identify all the ingredients of the smoothie he had drunk for breakfast.

Julian and I had rehearsed a punchy, prop-free explanation of our business and the encouraging results of our first couple of years of trading. We tried to impress them initially with the proposition without playing our ace, in the form of our publishing deal. Julian teed up the story of my chance encounter with Nigel and I tried to be amusing in describing his eccentricities. Cole, inches from my nostrils, did not move, but I heard little mutterings and tuts, suggesting that he was getting bored by a meandering anecdote. Eventually, he moved away from the orbit of my face, leant back in the sofa and, with some irritation, asked, "Is this story going anywhere?"

"Apologies," I replied confidently. "It is going to have a humdinger of a Hollywood ending, I promise."

"Well, we are not in Hollywood. Learn your California geography before pitching to us, please, Alex," said Brooke. A pointed insult cloaked with a beatific smile. Julian rolled his eyes, an unsubtle prompt for me to get to the point.

"All right, let me conclude. Clyde Pilestone has agreed to give us exclusive publishing rights to his next 'Resilient Martian' novel."

Like psychic twins, they snorted with laughter in unison.

"Sure, and Pope Francis has asked me to write his next sermon," Cole chirped.

"That's odd, because Barack Obama has asked me to give the next State of the Union," Brooke replied.

Julian, enjoying my humiliation, added his own unnecessary insult. "You're not the first to doubt him."

"Except," I shouted, "as my soon-to-be-ex-partner will attest, it's absolutely true. Perhaps we've come to the wrong obscenely large mansion to ask for money, if this is the level of derision we receive."

"Actually, it is true," added Julian sheepishly. "That's why we're here, and you should be very impressed."

Brooke and Cole stopped smiling and asked for further details, this time in a more professional tone. I outlined the deal and, with Julian chipping in, explained our need to fund rapid expansion to a number of global hubs very quickly. We were bombarded with questions, which we answered adroitly. After about half an hour, Cole clapped his hands to bring our initial interrogation to a close.

"So, guys, you stand before us asking for our money. Many have fallen at this stage. Brooke and I, as you can see, form a team that is indivisible. Two bodies with one brain, no one can separate our opinion." He paused and glanced casually over to his lovely wife, who nodded her head vigorously.

"We are a pretty formidable duo, you'll find," she added. It seemed odd that they had to assert their magnificence constantly. Their wealth was on tasteful display and their reputation globally revered, but still they felt compelled to pronounce their greatness. Cole continued to explain what lay ahead.

"We know you have a detailed business plan and we have more experts than you can imagine, who are going to pick holes to expose your beautiful baby to public scorn. We may even meet again just to publicly humiliate you in front of our team of sycophantic but extremely aggressive lawyers."

He was loving his power and nodded to Brooke to continue the performance.

"We like you, Alex and Julian, we really do. Moshe told us very little other than to meet you and give you lots of money before someone else did. You have gone further than hundreds of start-ups shoved our way every week. When we let you into our beautiful home, we expect you to be worth meeting."

Julian was about to say something, but realised that the performance should not be interrupted.

"Do you boys know what we like to do next?" Brooke asked teasingly. We shook our heads like well-trained puppies, unsure what was coming. They were a weird couple. At this point I was not ruling out a satanic mass or them singing a selection of show tunes.

"If we are going to give you a lot of money, then we need to believe that you are fighters and will make it really grow. We need to believe that you are truly competitive. Ambitious people have to win. There is no alternative to obsessively trying to get the better of an opponent."

Cole had got up and was walking to a modern, elegant mahogany bureau in the corner of the room. Talking to us over his shoulder, he took over from his wife and announced, "We are going to play a game. Me and Brooke versus you two. If you win, we may back you. If you fold, we will call you an Uber."

Julian and I exchanged bemused glances. Cole was opening a drawer and reaching for something. With the theatrical flourish of a failed actor, he pronounced, "Let the contest begin." He was holding a box in his hand. It was time for a rather unexpected game of Trivial Pursuit.

* * *

When I was fifteen, Nigel O'Connor dragged me for one of those inappropriate cinema trips, to endure Ingmar Bergman's 1957 Swedish masterpiece *The Seventh Seal*. I can still remember my incredulity as I tried, unsuccessfully, to stay awake for one hour and thirty-six minutes of black-and-white impenetrable expressionism. The plot remains hazy, but its central action involved a Crusader Knight's battle with Death over a game of chess. If Death won, the Knight perished. Watching the film was almost as painful as a mortal injury and I could not understand why it was revered by cinema buffs. It certainly put me off holidaying in Stockholm for a few years. However, as our unusual hosts bade us to sit at an enormous oak dining table and commence our own competition, I had a momentary vision of the chess game I had watched in the film. At the time, it seemed to be a highly risky strategy from the Knight, given his life was at stake. What if Death had read more chess books or had extra coaching?

And now I was going to play Trivial Pursuit to validate my competitive instinct in the quest for more cash. Brooke and Cole believed that if you were any good, you would win at all costs. This seemed to be an amoral but necessary philosophy if you wanted to achieve something of significance. I was outraged that it had come to this, but also quite excited. You see, as luck would have it, I was very poor at chess but extremely handy when it came to a general knowledge quiz.

Julian and I conferred with one another as Brooke fussed with drinks and snacks and Cole set up the board. We nonchalantly turned our backs on our hosts and, in stage whispers, tried to assess what lay ahead.

"We have met some nutters together," Julian muttered *sotto voce*, "but these may just be the biggest loons in the asylum."

"They're so mechanical in their behaviour. I'm not sure if it's an act or that they're a pair of robots." My excitement unfortunately made me inadvertently raise my voice and Cole seemed to stop in his tracks with a defiant look that suggested I had made him angry.

Julian was now irritated. "I bloody hate quizzes. I don't do trivia. I do long-form answers and elaborate strategies."

'Worry not!" I pronounced. "Do you know what my nickname at school was?"

"Alex the Arsehole?"

"No, the other one. They used to call me the General of Knowledge. I know my stuff. Don't worry your pretty head." I cracked my fingers with purpose, rolled my shoulders and thought about touching my toes. In truth, I wasn't sure what the appropriate warm-up was for competitive Trivial Pursuit.

Brooke handed us each some cold white wine and clinked the heavy crystal glasses with us, as if we were at a dinner party.

"*Santé.* May the worthiest win."

"Or just the robots," added a snarling Cole.

We sat down at the table, which had been set for quiz warfare with meticulous order. There were pads, pristine pencils arranged symmetrically and two boxes of questions, which seemed excessive, unless they were planning to play for the next three days straight.

"You'll be wondering why there are two boxes," said Cole on cue. "One is a UK edition and the other US. We realise that you know nothing about baseball, and we have very little interest in cricket, I can assure you. We have to make sure that it's a level playing field for either sport."

"That's very thoughtful," I said. "Perhaps I can explain some of the basic rules of cricket? It's so much more sophisticated than your national game of rounders."

It was an achievement to make Cole increasingly angry, but he frowned and muttered to himself, "Best game in the world, baseball. Arsehole."

Julian was evidently delighted by my enduring discomfort and announced with a smirk, "How odd, he knows your school nickname, Alex."

Brooke, sensing collective tetchiness, tried to shift the mood. "Boys. Boys. Let's calm it down a bit. We'll just have the anthems and then we can start."

Confused, I inadvertently looked around for signs that an invisible band was going to strike up the opening bars of 'The Star-Spangled Banner', but then saw the Johnsons laughing heartily at my expense.

"You see, Alex," Cole bellowed, "we Americans do have a sense of humour. Now, let's roll to start. Best of three games. First answer only and a minute per question. You have to answer as a team. Got it?" We nodded like obedient schoolboys.

And so, it began. I'd always associated the game with lazy Sunday afternoons in winter, fires blazing in the hearth, a cup of tea and a piece of home-made fruit cake. Lots of arguing, wrapped in the amiable competitiveness of family life. The only fruit cake today was Cole and there was no banter, only silence punctuated by the reading and answering of questions and some hushed conferring on answers. The house, nestling in a huge sequoia forest, was eerily still. A few minutes in and I felt tense. We had got off to a bad start as I made some poor calls.

"What year was *Lady Chatterley's Lover* published in the UK after D.H. Lawrence finished writing it in 1928?" said Brooke in a monotone.

"1930?" ventured Julian.

"No, it's a trick. It was banned for years – there was that high-profile trial in the 1960s. I'm going to say 1961."

Julian shrugged his assent and Cole, trying not to smile, replied with insincerity: "Sorry fella. You're a year out. It's 1960."

They then went on a pie spree (well, I don't know how else you describe the little segments you go around the board gathering) and quickly devoured a number of tricky questions.

"How many bones in a giraffe's neck – seven, fourteen, twenty-one or twenty-eight?" Who cares? But for future reference, the answer is the same as the human neck. Seven.

"Point to your septum, please, Cole." How ironic, given he was wearing a tee shirt that read 'Cocaine Made Me Rich'. As he placed a stubby finger to it, Brooke enthusiastically nabbed the little green Science and Nature piece.

After this, they stumbled over the literature question, which I asked doing my finest impression of Sir Ian McKellen: "Which character in Shakespeare's *Richard II* speaks of 'this sceptred isle… This blessed plot, this earth, this realm, this England'?"

Brooke looked to Cole with imploring eyes that seemed to say: *You were an actor once, you must know every Shakespeare play, just answer the question you schmuck.* Cole's swagger crumbled. He was embarrassed, and in the voice of a child floundering in class, he proffered an answer in hope rather than certainty.

"Falstaff?"

Without any triumphalism (well, a bit, I suppose), I told him the answer without even turning the card over. "Wrong play, mate. It was John of Gaunt. No need to check." Galvanised by this patriotic speech about home, I went for it big time, answering a host of questions without pausing or even looking to Julian for agreement.

"Kalahari." (Yes, that's where you find meerkats.)

"Moving Picture Experts Group." (If you wondered what MPEG stands for.)

"Perennial." (Not the quality of my jokes, but a plant that lives for more than two years.)

Despite me and mute Julian not knowing that Isaac Newton and Gottfried Leibniz both invented calculus, Brooke and Cole were unable to convert this final opportunity and garnered only a couple more bits of pie before failing with the US historical question of which Founding Father was born on the island of Nevis. Remember, it was only 2014 and *Hamilton* was not yet on Broadway.

We clinched the first game and the second game was something of a rout. I was galvanised and set a personal best (not that I had ever measured my performance before) with one sequence of nine successive questions. Eventually, we got to the final question on geography, needed to clinch victory. Cole, who by now exuded the resigned and disgruntled air of a man who would rather be in the dentist's chair than in our company, petulantly asked us the decisive question.

"Which is the highest capital city in the world?"

I smiled and turned to Julian, ready to embrace in victory.

"Got this one too, Julian. It's Addis Ababa."

"No, it's not."

"Honestly, go with me on this one. I've answered a version of this question before. Lots of people say Mexico City, and no one expects it to be Addis Ababa."

"And you're sure?"

"You bet. I know it because I once cheated in a quiz as a friend was setting the questions and gave me a few answers in advance. This was one of them."

Julian frowned with surprise. "Never had you down as a cheat, Alex. Didn't think you were nearly brave enough." He never missed an opportunity for a barbed comment.

"Nope, I'm a bone fide macho man, as you know, afraid of nothing. Now can we give the answer and win the game?"

"Well, tell me this, Einstein. Why, on my honeymoon, when I travelled through South America and arrived in La Paz, did every guidebook, hotel and street-corner sign say 'Welcome to the highest capital city in the world'? I spent most of the three days vomiting with altitude sickness. You are simply wrong."

I was now a bit discombobulated. After all, recalling trivia is instinctive. Your brain tells you immediately you have the correct answer or remains largely inactive if the question is unfamiliar. I remembered cheating when told the Addis Ababa answer, but now I wasn't sure of the actual question. Maybe it hadn't been the same? I ran my hand through my non-existent hair, a tic that always indicates anxiety.

"Perhaps you're correct? You've got me doubting now."

"I am. I can't name the cast of *EastEnders* like you, but I know when I'm right. It's a useful skill. You should learn it sometime."

"All right, we'll go with La Paz. *It's La Paz, in Bolivia*," I shouted so loudly I could be heard in New York.

Looking up at Brooke and Cole, they were sitting with arms firmly folded and totally expressionless. Cole reached over for the final blue wedge and, like a slow-motion mime artist, placed it in our counter. They stared at us, unblinking, in cold judgement.

After an age, Brooke's mouth was beginning to twitch. She was stifling a smile, and Cole could contain himself no further and began to laugh manically. Giants sobs of uncontrolled hysteria broke the hush. They were convulsing, trying to catch their breath between the spasms. Julian and I sat bemused. Eventually, Cole took a few yoga-like inhalations and spoke.

"And you thought I couldn't act. What a performance from us, Brooke."

"You nailed it, baby," said Brooke, giving him an exaggerated high five.

"What are you talking about?" asked Julian with rising irritation.

"We hate Trivial Pursuit."

"Worst game invented. So trite," added Brooke.

"Then why have we just played for two hours as if our lives depended on it?" I jumped in.

"Because, my little would-be entrepreneur… what a good way to see you two in action," Cole replied.

The penny dropped instantaneously for us both. This was not a test of our competitiveness but of our relationship. Brooke confirmed this when she added, 'We have learnt a lot, haven't we, Cole?"

"Certainly have. These two boys have given the game away."

"What game?" Julian asked timidly. He hated feeling vulnerable.

"Well, it's pretty obvious. Alex, you are very bright and have a head crammed with ideas and facts, but Julian, you are the strategic one," Brooke continued.

"And you are very competitive with each other. You both want to be right. Alex, you want to prove yourself to Julian. Julian, you really do look down on Alex." Cole finished the report with a *coup de grâce*.

"Your marriage is rather rocky, and you have simmering resentment for one another. You will need to make a big decision. Can you work through your problems or are you going to go your separate ways? Look at me and Brooke. We have the perfect marriage. It is an arrangement we have worked hard to craft. We even drafted a contract of conduct. You might want to consider doing the same?"

I couldn't now tell what Julian was thinking, but I wondered if he felt the same as me. We'd been undressed in public and it was embarrassing. Brooke smiled in victory, but then brought us back to the reason we were sitting there in the first place.

"Anyway, you'll be wanting to know our decision. Subject to scrutiny of your numbers and your agreement to have some mentoring on your relationship, we love PrimaParent. I mean, come on. You have persuaded Clyde Pilestone to commit publishing suicide. You guys are the real deal."

"Congratulations, guys," added Cole with new-found warmth. I reflected that asking for money was becoming a ritual humiliation. Test after test from powerful people, pretending to be one thing in order to assess how good we really were. Why did the need for funding entail a series of conversations with fragile and complicated egos more interested in game-playing than business-building?

Several celebratory hours later, drained and emotionally exposed, Julian and I sat in a taxi back to our hotel. We had the money. It was just contingent on the promise we had made to have couples therapy.

15. Uncivil Partnership

"A coach, let me tell you, Alex, is something a football team uses to get to a match. I am not going to embark on some touchy-feel examination of our relationship. I managed to avoid Catherine's pleas to speak to someone to save our marriage and I have no intention of starting with you."

It was three weeks after our trip to California and we had just received final notification of major funding from the Johnsons, having finished a video call with their phalanx of lawyers, advisors and accountants. Cole had announced that we were good to go, and the posse of suits and buttoned-down shirts had broken into whoops and cries of enthusiasm as if they had just won a major sporting event. There were only five of us at the other end of the call, sitting with awkward English restraint. We produced a ripple of applause as if at a piano recital.

There had been one unusual contractual stipulation, the product of our bizarre character examination. Julian and I had to produce a quarterly report from some form of executive coach, who would verify that our business partnership was functioning. They wanted to check we were more Ben & Jerry than Tom & Jerry.

I had researched potential candidates and wanted to review them with Julian to start the process. The thought of agnostic adjudication of our increasingly strained partnership was horrendous. Julian's ego and lack of empathy were to blame. Everyone could see that. Still, a deal was a deal and we wanted to progress with the support of the Johnsons, even if it meant some excruciating sessions for the two of us. Julian, however, was not so willing to be flexible or obedient to the ludicrous demands of our new backers and would not read the profiles of the individuals I was presenting to him. Like a child refusing to eat his broccoli, he was not that reasonable. After a little bit of back and forth, he folded his arms and stated: "You could tell me Steve Jobs had risen from the dead to give us an individual masterclass. I would still say no."

"What do we do, then, to meet that particular clause in the contract? You know, that irritating little piece of paper that reminds us of our legal responsibilities."

"You have no imagination."

"And you have no scruples. Let's call it an honourable draw."

"No, I know what I'm saying. You are totally blinkered by obeying the rules. That's why you need me so much, to show you how to break a few."

"All right, Che Guevara. I get it. You foment revolutions and dismantle the establishment. May I remind you, though, Brooke and Cole will dismantle us if we don't do what we've promised."

"Relax. We will absolutely send them a report. We'll just take turns to write it and it'll make us seem so adoring of one another, they'll suspect we're lovers."

"It's a bit high-risk, isn't it?"

"It's less risky than actually meeting with someone who tells Brooke and Cole the truth about us. Besides, you'd probably spend a real session in tears, and how awkward would that be for everyone?"

"You make a fair point."

I paused. It was dishonest but extremely attractive, and meant my feelings would remain hidden and Julian's could remain buried beneath a ton of non-emotional concrete. He had it all worked out.

"Very simple. We get one of the team to build a website for a fictitious coach and we make it look like we're using someone very impressive but discreet. Then we write a compelling description of a session in which you reveal that you're in awe of me, can't deal with your sense of inadequacy when in the same room. Well, that's my starter for ten anyway, but I think it's pretty spot on."

Amoral, yes, but very compelling. We would control the narrative and avoid unsettling our new backers. Brooke and Cole had given us $15m for effectively a 10 per cent share of our business, based on an agreed valuation of $150m. Thanks to Clyde Pilestone, we were now major players and did not need our squabbles to undermine our ebullience.

"OK, you may be on to something. But I want editorial control. If I do it, I'll make us sound normal. If you draft it, you'll deliberately make me sound like I'm a sociopath. But this has to be our secret and completely protected. They'll shut us down if they find out."

"They're not going to find out. They'll look for an endorsement that we're functioning well together. They're not going to care where we're going to have our psyches probed."

As luck would have it, we didn't need to invent a coach and mentor. No, we went one better. We bribed someone to let us write the reports, which she would send on our behalf. Dr Erika McNab was the younger sister of Julian's mother's best friend. (Do try to keep up.) She had spent her life as a CEO in the male-dominated sector of oil and gas, commodities and derivatives, and was now a highly respected non-exec director, coach and mentor. Fortunately, she loved opera even more than she did professional rectitude. Julian somehow managed to persuade her that regular tickets to the Royal Opera House and Glyndebourne would be adequate recompense for kindly sending an email four times a year to the Johnsons.

A month or so after receiving the first instalment of our money, we sent a three-page detailed summary of a meeting that never happened. The concluding paragraph was carefully constructed by me late one night to be credibly compelling and establish a narrative that outlined our bogus commitment to self-improvement:

> I asked Julian and Alex to restate their objectives for our future sessions and their answers attested to a realisation that their working compatibility and interdependent skills were strong, but their desire for leadership pre-eminence needed to be lessened to ensure a more supportive partnership.
>
> Alex stated: 'You know Julian and I can get quite tetchy at times and this is not always helpful, but it comes from a place of mutual respect and we have to be more mindful that we are co-CEOs. One of us is not more important than the other.'
>
> Julian added: 'I really think I am better working with Alex than I am working on my own. I suppose years of being sent away to school and trying to prove myself has made me a bit ruthlessly independent. I welcome your help in addressing this.'

How ironic. Just as this beautifully crafted fiction about our healthy and respectful relationship was being sent to our unsuspecting backers, it was in reality beginning to disintegrate like a sandcastle at high tide.

* * *

During the Christmas holidays, I took some time off to reconnect with my family. The children thought I was a soldier returning from an obscure war: they knew they had seen me before, they just couldn't quite place where. I was exhausted from the year and spent much of the time in a state of narcolepsy, dozing whenever I stopped moving for a second. The morning was crisp and clear, and we all sat at breakfast, dappled in wintry sunshine, momentarily becalmed as a family. I was enjoying a breakfast with the kids of all manner of inappropriate sugar-based delicacies in the hope that the energy rush would sustain me through an impending visit from Sarah's mother. My lovely wife was ensconced in a rare child-free moment and pored over the paper, oblivious to the Coco-Pops carnage I was creating.

"Bastard. Bastard. Bastard!" she suddenly screamed.

"Steady on. I'm just giving the kids their breakfast," I replied instinctively.

"Not you. Julian."

"What are you talking about?"

She tossed the paper to me angrily, as if I had been responsible for whatever she'd just read. The headline simply stated: 'Lucy Reveals New Beau', and below it was a picture of the gorgeous award-winning, Oxford-educated, RSC-trained, Hollywood-blockbuster star Lucy Vogel. She was on a red carpet promoting her latest movie, and standing with his arm draped protectively around her was the handsome, immaculately dressed, stubbly-faced Julian. I felt a ripple of instinctive jealously as I sat in my Bart Simpson tee shirt and tatty boxers. I'd never look that good. The accompanying text box contained little copy:

BAFTA-winning actress Lucy Vogel introduced her new boyfriend to the press at the premiere in Leicester Square of her latest film, To Love Another. *He is Julian Lloyd-Mason, 38, founder and CEO of the website PrimaParent.com.*

"You're right," I said angrily. "He is a total bastard."

"At last," sighed Sarah, "you can see it."

"I mean, why would he call himself founder and CEO? He's co-founder and co-CEO."

Sarah looked at me with an expression of resigned disappointment and then muttered loudly under her breath, prompting ever-alert Theo to shout enthusiastically, "Mummy's just called Daddy the F-word."

I realised that perhaps I'd put my self-interest and vanity in front of the correct response from a sensitive and loving husband. It was lucky I hadn't articulated the other thought that had crossed my mind, which was that we'd got some pretty good free publicity in a national newspaper.

"You're right, of course. It's pretty disgraceful parading himself so smugly. How horrible for Catherine." That's always what a shallow bloke like me thinks when they see a friend escorting a beautiful movie star.

"Look, Alex, everyone knew Julian would move on in minutes. But he looks so pleased with himself. It's like he's telling Catherine, *Sorry, love, but I just had to upgrade.*" I nodded and admitted to her what I was actually feeling.

"That's the thing about Julian. He seems to be able to operate above us all. He's a sort of magnet for glamour and success, but oblivious to damaging people along the way. I'm always ducking and diving to avoid being the next casualty." It sounded like I was paraphrasing something I had once read.

Sarah was not impressed by my explanation. She turned her back on me to prove the point that, once again, I did not have quite the empathy she expected. Tutting to herself as she turned the page of the paper, she simply muttered, "I just hope she dumps him for a much more muscular leading man on her next film."

* * *

Several days later, we all returned to the office to start a new year of graft. Grabbing coffees, Alice and I sat down to compare notes on our few days away.

"It wasn't so great for me this year," Alice bemoaned. "You know, however long I've been with Caroline, whenever we go to my parents, they still can't quite accept the relationship. They love their grandchildren — I just get the impression they would prefer them to be raised by heterosexual criminals than a couple of lesbians who like to hold hands in public."

"Sounds a bit like my relationship with Sarah's mother. She would happily take a murderer who works nine-to-five over me, I'm sure."

"My mother kept trying to pretend to be understanding and worldly, but unfortunately she blew it when she asked Caroline if she was very active in the Lesbian G&T + community."

Our laughter was muffled by the clunking grating of the lift arriving, its cables groaning under the weight of the task. This year we really needed to get an engineer round to look at trying to oil a cable or two. The door opened and Julian emerged with a flourish, as if expecting applause. He was pristine in clothes that looked like they had come straight out of the new Armani 'my other half is actually a famous movie star' range. Seeing us sequestered with our coffees in the corner, he marched towards us with an expression of unbridled self-satisfaction.

"Happy New Year, co-workers. Did Santa get you everything on your list?" He hugged us both, which certainly caught Alice by surprise.

"I think he missed me out this year," I said. "He was too busy making your dreams come true." Alice and I hadn't discussed Julian's new domestic arrangement, but she clearly knew about it too, because she mischievously put on a simpering luvvie voice, wiped a few invisible tears from her cheek and pronounced: "*And I couldn't have won this Oscar without the love of my partner and guide in life, Julian. This is for you.*" She thrust an imaginary statuette in the air and blew a few kisses to no one in particular.

Julian clutched his stomach and said with adolescent sarcasm, "You two are just beyond funny. Come to think of it, what lies beyond *funny*? Oh yes, *unfunny*."

I raised my hand, as if to say it was time for a truce, and continued, "Well, Julian, we're just very proud of you for finding a way of getting our name in the papers. Smart move. And when we've sold the business, you can dump her as she'll no longer serve a purpose."

"Or I can stay with her and just dump you for a vaguely competent partner." As ever with Julian, the distinction between banter and nastiness was hard to see. Aware that perhaps he had overreacted, he put a placatory hand on my arm and looked at us both wistfully.

"Right, chaps, let's stop all this joking. I know my new public profile has an impact on the business, good and bad. It certainly made for a tricky Christmas for me."

"How has Catherine reacted?" I asked, knowing full well what the answer would be.

"Let's just say, she has a few bits of crockery missing now. Luckily, I have good reactions and she has a pretty poor aim."

"You didn't tell her about your new relationship before you stepped on a red carpet with a huge movie star in front of the entire world?" asked Alice with incredulity.

"Please don't judge me, Alice, it's not your place."

"How was the film, anyway?" I chipped in, trying to change the subject.

"Loved it, although it's a bit weird watching your new girlfriend have sex with another man on an IMAX screen. I suppose I'll have to get used to it. You should see her next role."

We were all silent, not really sure what to say. Fame and celebrity were quite seductive to me and I was fascinated by the implications of Julian's new life. What would it be like to be recognised? How could you enjoy a quiet meal ever again? I wondered if my profile would change when we published *The Galaxy Slayer's Last Stand*. I suppose my ambition was fuelled by some rather unimpressive vanity too.

The nice part of me, buried deep but still flickering with light occasionally, knew that Julian was something of a cad. He had impeccable manners but shoddy values. By now it was clear that, for him, dealing with Catherine was an inconvenient rather than remorseful experience.

Alice announced that she had proper work to do and walked away from us. Julian gestured towards The Bored Room, shutting the door after me. I wasn't sure if I was going to be told off or he was going to show me photos on his phone of his new glamour-filled life.

"Listen, mate," he began breezily, "I just wanted to inform you that I'm going to need to take some money out of the business."

"Does Lucy have expensive tastes, then? Shame, you used to love a trip to Pizza Hut."

"Catherine has cut up very rough. I'm going to have some hefty legal bills pretty quickly."

What to do? Part of me felt an unexpected wave of sympathy for him. Perhaps he was going to have to fight unceremoniously for some tenuous access to his children. However, his request also made me very uneasy. After all, we were raising money to grow the business and most certainly not to spend on ourselves.

"Julian. That's a tricky request, isn't it? You know that Moshe or the Johnsons are not going to feel that positive towards you if they think they're spending money on your custody battle?"

"Why do they have to be told?"

"Because I don't want to build a business where we lie to the people who back us." I said this with spontaneous conviction. I was clear that Julian could not deviate from our agreed remuneration plans.

"That's your view. I've put everything into the business for the last two years. I've made sacrifices and now you won't listen. Look, just because you and saintly Sarah have a perfect marriage doesn't mean that it's easy for everyone else. I'm asking for some help, Alex. This won't happen that often, I can assure you."

"What do you want me to say? Of course I want to be helpful. I'm just not sure that we can do this right now."

He got up to leave and the familiar froideur returned. "In truth, I'm not that bothered by your concerns, but I wanted to see if there was any possibility for future friendship between us. Don't stress about our backers. I've actually contacted them all and told them what I need. The money shouldn't be a problem at all."

With that, he left the room without looking back.

* * *

Our new finance director had been with us for a few months by that time. After we'd dismissed Simon, Alice and I had led a search for someone with more probity, experience and basic arithmetic skills. The process had been rather torturous as every time we found a candidate we liked, Julian exercised his veto with gusto. His objections were often spurious, but hard to override. One candidate was dismissed because he had a quiet and slightly timid voice, irrelevant to his unquestionable competence but for Julian an illustration of what he called 'reckless indecision'.

In the end, our pressing need for financial leadership outweighed the barrage of objections that Julian consistently fired our way. We appointed Samantha Lane, who, having worked for another successful start-up, the fitness app runfurther, was seduced by our energy and success. She was proving a dependable and extremely smart addition to the team. Her elegant calmness was sorely tested several days after my confrontation with Julian, when she received an email that prompted her to find me and ask if we could go out of the office to discuss something.

It was unfortunately snowy and freezing that morning, so our discreet getaway was slightly undone by being forced to put on our hefty coats and scarfs and then wait for a minute until the world's noisiest lift could announce to the office that we were leaving it together. We sat in a nearby café in a quiet corner. She handed me a printed email.

"What is going on, please, Alex?"

The email was from Julian to Samantha and was copied to all our principal investors. My name was conspicuously absent.

Samantha,

Please transfer £50,000 to my personal account forthwith. The sum is to be deducted from all future dividend payments to me and should be recorded as such. Approval has been received from above investors.

Julian

There were three other emails from our investors, which all contained the single word 'Approved'. I didn't know what to say to Samantha other than that I felt more emasculated than ever by Julian's single-minded pursuit of his own needs.

In the end, clouded by anger and frustration, I simply said, "I suppose he's using a very expensive lawyer and Catherine is pretty angry."

"That's irrelevant. You can't be a start-up and use your seed capital as a personal loan. What next? He wants to buy a new car? He wants to hire a yacht to impress his new lady?"

"You are, of course, right. I just wish he'd involved me in the discussion. I'm going to speak to them all and check that he's told them the truth in full."

"You do that, Alex. You're going to need to stand up to him or he'll take everything." She was not just a good finance director but an accurate judge of character.

* * *

"Moshe, Happy New Year. Hope it's a good one for us all." I started the conversation an hour later in as light a fashion as I could.

'What do you want, Alex?" he replied curtly. 'I am in the middle of signing a big deal with the government. I haven't got time for you now."

"I'll be quick. Did you agree to Julian's loan? I want to know that you're genuinely on board."

"If you are asking me the question, then you know the answer and have seen my email."

"And you are happy to support his divorce lawyers with your money."

"You know, perhaps it is time for you to realise something, Alex."

"Tell me."

"You have a partner who will be more successful than you because he doesn't rely on his conscience to tell him what he needs to do. He does as he pleases. We all work like that – me, George, Brooke and Cole. But not, it seems, you."

"That's your view. I'm only concerned that the money we've worked so hard to secure is not being used to build the company. You can keep telling me I'm too weak, but I want to understand why Julian is doing this with your blessing."

Moshe paused for a moment. I wasn't sure if he'd put me on mute to continue another conversation or was simply revelling in a crude demonstration of his power. When he spoke, it was softly.

"Listen carefully. Julian will destroy you if you let him. You need to fight to hold on to what you are building. Yes, I have let him have the money and it is outrageous, but I have spoken to the Johnsons and George. We agreed to let him progress. We did it, though, because we want to see how you will respond."

"What do you mean?"

"It might well be that PrimaParent doesn't have room for two leaders. It is time to put the two angry dogs in a sack and see who comes out barking." With that, the phone clicked silent and he was gone. I didn't know if the reference to dogs was a well-known homily. I just knew it was time to sharpen my claws.

* * *

Julian and I were stiffly formal with one another for the following few days. We sat in meetings in happy agreement, carrying on superficially as if we were an effective and collaborative team. It seemed pointless to do anything different. But, like a true obsessive, I continually devised stratagems for self-preservation. I was never very good at chess. I would get bored and my limited attention span would struggle to plan moves in advance. But I knew that I was like the medieval Knight playing chess against Death in that pretentious Swedish film I mentioned. One bad move and it was a life in entrepreneurs' hell for me.

I was consoled by the fact that the business respected Julian, but he was not particularly liked. He had the cavalier brusqueness of a bullying sixth-form prefect. If he was nice to you, your self-esteem was bolstered. If he was irritated, his charm was eclipsed by a mocking cruelty. Julian's nastiness was gender-neutral. Tears were commonplace among our less robust team members and my shoulder, offered in times of need, was becoming increasingly damp.

Nothing was said until a few weeks later when we stood in strained silence making ourselves an early morning coffee. Julian, in a voice brimming with insincerity, started off the conversation by asking me, "How are Sarah and the kids? You haven't regaled us with a charming anecdote about your domestic happiness for a while."

"All good, thank you. How's your divorce going?" I retorted.

"Yup, progressing with the lawyers. These things take time."

"Well, I hope the money doesn't run out. I know divorces can be expensive."

We looked at each other intently. You very rarely stare straight into someone's eyes and try not to avert your gaze. Embarrassment tends to prevail. But that winter's morning, with our business about to catapult to global recognition, we stood like boxers at a weigh-in, nose-to-nose and unblinking.

Julian broke first. He smiled, slapped me on the back collegiately and said with a broad grin, "Bring it on, Alex, that's what I say. Bring it on."

PART 3

GLOBAL CONFLICT

16. A Kind of Madness

What is ambition?

When I met a stranger in a park and unburdened my career aspirations, how could I have anticipated the successful chaos that would envelop me? It's hard to unravel the exact emotions that motivated me to sacrifice stability for uncertainty. Perhaps if I'm honest, what rose above the general quest for a lucrative commercial enterprise was the need for massive external recognition. I wanted people who knew me to jealously spit out their cornflakes when they saw my huge profile in the weekend papers.

Ambition has traditionally engendered conflict and suffering. The Old Testament is basically a long prohibition for man not to elevate aspiration above devotion to God. Eve tempted Adam with the apple and look how well that turned out. Jacob stole his brother Esau's birthright, demonstrating that convention need not stand in the way of getting what you want. His son Joseph, empowered by self-belief, accurately told his brothers that they would one day bow down to him, because he was superior and destined for greater things, which, as you will know if you've seen the musical, is what happened.

Look at its Latin root and you will see that ambition is a political aspiration and a lust for power. *Ambitio* was used in Rome almost exclusively in the context of public life. In its earliest iteration the word had the literal sense of 'to go around', and referred to the politician on the make soliciting or canvassing votes.

Ancient learning is steeped in warnings of the dangers of ambition. We were taught to restrain our quest for more because it did not necessarily deliver contentment or inner peace. Somewhere in history, however, this view was submerged and forgotten beneath the advance of an industrialised society and the new opportunities it afforded for prosperity.

The US is the greatest exemplar of this shift. Founded by Puritans who taught ascetic restraint, the post-1776 emergence of an independent country in which every man was equal (except for the slaves) gave rise to the American Dream. No matter where you came from, you were taught to believe in your limitless potential – the very epitome of the equality of ambition. Studies show, however, that for all the advancement and improvement in quality of life in the last fifty years of the twentieth century, people in America were no happier at its end than at its midpoint.

And then finally consider the most famous artists, writers, actors and musicians you can think of and everything you know of their turbulent histories. Greatness and posterity are often intertwined with lives of excess. Infidelity, substance abuse and mental fragility are often indistinguishable from the relentlessness of great talent. Wanting and needing more from creative success can bring with it sustained unhappiness.

Why is all this relevant? In retrospect, there was evidence all round me that proved ambition was no guarantee of future happiness. I was, however, too excited by the adrenaline release of our rapid expansion and too focused on succeeding to realise this.

* * *

Our expansion was faster than anyone could have anticipated. We received more money from Moshe and from Brooke and Cole, as well as a little bit of additional Silicon Valley support, which the Johnsons had corralled. George, to my surprise, had at the last minute matched Moshe's contribution, without much explanation. Julian put it down to his paranoia at being outflanked by a rival.

Empowered by newly restored cash balances, we were able to spread out across the globe like a conquering army with full bellies and shiny new armour.

In our third year of trading, things got serious. We rapidly grew to over three hundred employees, initially in six locations, and had to bring in all sorts of new skills that we hadn't anticipated. A robust sales team to carry on securing an endless supply of sellers and retailers to our site was a top priority. We grew our marketing team to include content producers and designers, as well as the best digital marketers around. Our high-profile and rapid progress meant that people wanted to work for us, so recruitment could be done at speed with a willing pool of hungry individuals ready to join our cult.

We had to grow up as an organisation, even if we were still running around in short trousers. Like all visionary digital businesses, we defined success by the breadth of the talent we hired and our ability to persuade people to precipitously leave secure jobs. I was particularly excited that some of these people were even over thirty and remembered vinyl first time round. Of necessity, we also recruited a robust legal team in case they turned nasty and tried to sue us.

I concentrated on building our international teams by finding leaders who we could trust to colonise other markets with speed and efficiency. Each of these appointments was a leap of faith akin to a bungee jump with a cord no one had checked. We did not know when we appointed Manuel Garrido, our Spanish CEO, for example, if he was *mucho bueno* or *mucho crapo*. Each time, I would fly in and out of capital cities, meet a couple of people and make a decision on these lieutenants based on finely honed instincts. (*Did they speak English? Did they like coffee? When could they start?*) They were given a budget, a launch manual, and a welcome bottle of cava, and expected to report back confidently each month on their nascent progress.

The area that required the most scrutiny was Dimitri's team. Over three years, he had really changed. The naive and endearing optimism had calcified into a charmless focus that made him extremely intimidating and challenging. His rigidity meant that he would only be available for meetings or conversations at fixed times during the week, which we always had to accommodate. It was still worth the effort, because the increasing complexity of the business represented a challenge he was obsessed with overcoming. The more difficult personal interaction became, the greater our confidence in his delivery.

There were lots of practical challenges. His team required nurturing and significant emotional support. We had to confront dangerous levels of stress and anxiety among a talented but bruised cohort, working ridiculous hours while desperately hoping for a crumb of approbation and endorsement from Dimitri, the cruellest taskmaster imaginable. Simmering discontent often festered into complaints, which we had to settle quickly. We threw money at people to make sure they were a bit happier and to dampen any litigious inclinations.

Dimitri had settled into a relationship with one of his team, a developer from Poland called Lena. When the romance became clearly serious to everyone in the office, we hoped that it might soften his robotic interactions with us. Unfortunately, it just created two Dimitris. When Lena was near him, he simpered affectionately with no regard to what this looked like. When she was not there, he morphed back into his chilly totalitarian persona.

The nature of all of our relationships evolved a little as we moved from start-up informality to a business that had to behave with more structure and process. For Julian and me, this rapid scaling-up provided a temporary truce in our frosty relationship. We became more effective co-leaders, spending less time together, relying on the other to ease the burden of a mountainous to-do list. I drove the vision for the business, its proposition and external promotion, encouraging values that at least made us an enjoyable place to work. Julian did deals. He loved the negotiation, the intractable posturing and the close. Entertainment, retailing, publishing – Julian tenaciously delivered exciting content to our site and revelled in the elaborate ruses and tactics he employed to ensure favourable terms.

Alice was our backbone. She became the chief operating officer with oversight of everything. With a remarkable ability to know exactly what was going on, she would arrive like a cuddly marine to dispense practical assistance to any ailing individual in need of support. Everyone respected Alice and did what she asked. She didn't crave recognition, but derived satisfaction from calming the chaos generated by the rest of us. Even Julian, so prickly and dismissive initially, turned to her continually for advice. I would also avoid making the simplest decision without recourse to her opinion. She would tell me when I was behaving badly or insensitively and developed a bespoke 'twatometer' that measured my stupidity at any given time. When she rated me six or above, which happened regularly, I was contractually bound to reverse any decision I had made.

We had formal management and board meetings and ensured that agendas, reports and financial overviews were consistently produced to the satisfaction of our backers and investors. With the expectation of much higher levels of governance, we rehearsed our presentations carefully and tried to minimise the spin. We even got ourselves some bright graduate personal assistants to manage our diaries after the time I accidently arrived in Frankfurt to interview a potential country manager who was waiting for me in a bar in Paris. Childish tantrums were replaced by the swagger of success as we strode through the office saying good morning to growing teams of people whose names we did not know.

We naturally outgrew our office too. After a couple of years, we ran out of desk space, quickly realising that short of colonising

Starbucks next door, we needed to take drastic action, as apparently shoving four interns in a stationery cupboard was not good practice.

As ever, Julian and I could not agree on a location as we focused on finding somewhere convenient for our own homes. I wanted somewhere en route to North London, and Julian, now an established movie-star appendage, was firmly ensconced in Holland Park and therefore expected my compliance to his needs. In the end, we had a bit of good fortune. George Dobson called in a favour from a fellow property developer, who gave us a deal on space in a new building in King's Cross. We took two floors with an immediate option on a couple more if needed. It was modern and minimalist, with excellent infrastructure. The lifts glided noiselessly so you could arrive at work without the accompanying metallic symphony.

In 2015, King's Cross was rapidly becoming a new media hub, buzzing with the excitement of technological advancement. When I was a child, the area was only associated with trains to the North and seedy kerb-crawlers around the back of York Way. Somehow, we were going to become a fixture in this most modern of tech campuses. Corporations were now communities that had everything you needed, so you could work a sixteen-hour day and have all your needs catered for without leaving your hot-desk.

We moved on a muggy summer's day with military precision orchestrated by Alice, whose favourite term of all time was 'complicated logistics'. By the afternoon, we had a functioning office, swaying rhythmically as they clicked and clacked on their keyboards to the Ibiza mix being pumped through our invisible speaker network. Julian and I stood by a huge seventh-floor window and surveyed chic London flowing beneath us.

"Did you ever think we would get here so quickly?" he asked contemplatively.

'Well, the Northern Line is pretty reliable these days," I replied.

His eyebrows arched slightly in irritation. He pressed on. "We're at the centre of it all. It's kind of appropriate that we're right by the railway that connected the industrial North to London in Victorian times. This place is all about change and the future."

"You wait until Google move in. We won't be able to move for badly dressed developers."

"You'll fit in very well."

"Thank you. I'm sure they have some Lord Lucan lookalikes too, so you can feel at home." My jokes about his aristocratic mien tended not to elicit a response, but this time it unsettled him.

"Alex, Lord Lucan tried to kill his wife. I just want to divorce mine elegantly, without recourse to any violence. Anyway, no point getting philosophical, you'll just make a crass joke. Put simply, I am very excited about the future."

"As am I, you old sentimentalist." Sidling up next to him, I put my arm affectionately around his shoulders. He stiffened instinctively.

* * *

We now had 10,000 sellers in the UK and over 250,000 subscribers. All our numbers steadily increased each week. More people engaged with the site, spent longer searching, and booked or ordered something as a consequence. The average value of a transaction increased, the number of transactions made by each customer increased and the frequency of these transactions increased, as did the breadth of categories customers would search for. The more you engaged with PrimaParent, the more it learnt about your behaviour and served you offers on things you would like. It was an ever-expanding universe with limitless potential.

We now had banks of fresh-faced graduates selling the site to lots of businesses up and down the country. Some were happy to have a job to pay back mountainous student debt and gave it their all. Others would arrive with an air of bewildered disdain that after an illustrious academic career, they were reduced to persuading a clown in Grimsby (a real, not a metaphorical one) to join our digital community. We gave them all sales training and scripts to follow. I would often hear the refrain 'Can you risk not being a part of PrimaParent?' as I walked past, and realised that it was just our version of *And do you want fries with that?*

Growth. Growth. Growth. The sales team made phone call after phone call and sent email after email in search of new recruits. At the bottom of our social order, we trained and flogged them hard, then let them leave the moment they could find a job more worthy of their under-utilised talents. A few genuinely loved selling and stayed with us. You could tell them easily because they dressed smartly and brushed their hair, half expectant that we would one day send them out to actually meet someone.

Next up the ladder were our digital marketers, bombarding an infinite universe with solicitations for subscriptions. This cohort was filled with individuals of enormous energy and a vocational focus. If Facebook or Google changed an algorithm, it was their role to explain the implications to the senior citizens like me. One of them, a year out of university, looked at me once with a condescending smile and said: "How could you really understand this, Alex? You probably didn't get your first iPhone until you were thirty."

At the top of our stratified organisation came Dimitri and his team of coders, developers, data scientists, front-end and back-end designers and engineers. They were the First Estate and as far as they were concerned everyone else could eat cake, although it would have to be gluten-free and vegan. They knew that sales and marketing people simply sold what they created. Anyone could do that, but few could build something from nothing. Under Dimitri's vicious tutelage, if asked to comply with an inconvenient deadline by an intellectual inferior, they folded their arms and stared defiantly at the pond life who had challenged them until they slunk away sheepishly, preferably in tears.

Our model had evolved since our initial plan and we were about to become a publishing and entertainment hub. While Nigel O'Connor was firing his laser-powered intergalactic blaster at the cowering publishing world, we had to rapidly develop infrastructure to ensure we could deliver his latest masterpiece to an expectant global following. We started by hiring the best publishing talent we could find, from agents to editors, and told them to abandon the stale security of established businesses to join our aggressive band of literary bandits.

Inevitably, the publishing team were a bit different from the rest of the crowd. To start with, they could all speak in perfectly constructed sentences. The influence of my academic father has meant a basic respect for the written and spoken word, an antediluvian concept in my own business. (It means 'before the Flood' – look it up.) No one bothered with punctuation and spelling on emails, with the exception of a few editorial staff. My puritanical streak was exacerbated by the inability of anyone to speak a sentence that did not have 'like' in front of at least every other word. Could they not hear themselves? *We are like nearly ready to like launch and are like doing a couple of like checks to see if it like launches.* What are you talking about, are we launching or not?

Julian secured some great deals with various authors who were going to develop content for us. We had a very clever idea to create a 'Brilliant Book of the Month', which would allow us to deliver a unique reading experience and to generate noise around each launch. Another coup was that we paid £150,000 to secure the rights to the out-of-print 'The Adventures of the Templar Knights', a series of nine books written between 1942 and 1967 by retired naval officer Commander T. Wallace. My sister and I had loved these stories about medieval rampaging knights battling against a variety of enemies in pursuit of divine truth. Somehow the publishing world felt that they were inappropriate to a modern sensibility. With judicious editing to remove a few politically incorrect terms for Turks, Jews and the French, we were left with a rollicking set of adventure stories told in a surprisingly modern style. The author's estate couldn't believe it when we approached them, and we couldn't believe how cheaply they gave it away.

* * *

I marvelled at how we had evolved rapidly from a scrappy start-up into a global operation, making things up as we went along. We decided that prior to the launch of *The Galaxy Slayer's Last Stand*, we should get the whole company together for a corporate group hug. We now had nearly fifty international staff and flew them in on a fleet of dodgy cheap flights at unsociable hours. We hired a recently refurbed independent cinema to present our vision to everyone and then planned a massive party.

The presentation had become an ego-fuelled battle between me and Julian. I wanted to convey ruthless parity. He wanted to clearly demonstrate that there was only one real CEO worth listening to at PrimaParent. For a week we sat disagreeing, but in the end I managed to persuade him that we should present together and try to recreate some of the amiable banter of previous events. With Alice's prompting, he reluctantly agreed, and I produced a script that magnanimously gave him some of the best lines.

It was a gloriously sunny day in July 2015 as we all gathered at the cinema, mingling over a breakfast of smoothies, organic yogurt bowls, croissants and coffee. I was meeting people from our new offices whose names I had seen on spreadsheets, but not met in person. They were full of earnest enthusiasm, which I actually found quite humbling, remembering that this all began only three years previously on a park bench by a sandpit, while chatting to a stranger. As the founder, I was treated with a mix of reverence and polite respect. They all wanted to make a good impression and I quickly got used to a lot of vigorous nodding in agreement with everything I said.

We adjourned to the plush reclining seats in the giant cinema space. Julian and I took our places, ready to make our appearance. The proceedings were compèred by two members of the marketing team, Ami and Harvey. She was a budding stand-up in her spare time, and he was an established DJ. We had agreed that they could have as much fun in their introductions as they wanted. This included, of course, our walk-on music.

The lights dimmed and a video montage of twenty-four hours in the life of PrimaParent burst on to the screen. Lots of high-definition shots of people waving in all of our different offices across the globe, larking around in meeting rooms, shoving people in bins, pouring glasses of water on unsuspecting colleagues' heads. The climax was an unforgettably inappropriate shot of seven of Dimitri's team in London, who conveyed their diverse international backgrounds by standing in a line and dropping their trousers, to reveal the flags of their country of origin painted on their naked buttocks. The soundtrack was the Henry Hall Orchestra's 1932 'Teddy Bear's Picnic', adding an ironic counterbalance to this most youthful depiction of a company that created happy memories for children. It was then our turn. Ami first introduced Julian.

"PrimaParent global family, please put your hands together for our founder. The man who makes Prince Harry look common. A man so good-looking that you won't want to stand next to him. A man of impeccable taste. A man of style. A man of the people.

Well, a man of the rich people anyway. Let's all bow down to the always classy… Julian Lloyd-Mason."

As Julian stood up, the classic TV theme from *Brideshead Revisited* accompanied him on his journey to the stage. It was not energetic, but it had an appropriateness to Julian's innate elegance. He walked in a measured fashion, waving regally and even bowing a couple of times with faux humility. He was always happy to be praised for his looks and breeding. I grew a little nervous and wondered if I should have retained full editorial control for my introduction. Harvey smiled mischievously.

"And now, colleagues, it is time to meet our other founder. This man has a style all of his own and perhaps it would be better sometimes if it did not leave the house. This man's jokes will make you cry. Not with laughter, though. This man has so many ideas a day he doesn't know what to do with them, and it is just our bad luck that they come our way. He really cares about what he does. He just cares even more about what people think. Please put your hands together for our loveable leader… Alex Lazarus."

Slightly reeling from the derogatory remarks and wondering if Julian had somehow intervened, I stood up before the music began. I knew I was in trouble, I just didn't expect the 1961 Henry Mancini theme 'Baby Elephant Walk'. If you're unfamiliar with it, it's very catchy, but it's not the theme of a titan of the digital revolution. I didn't know what to do but, not wanting to appear irritated, I tried to be a good sport. My walk, unfortunately, though not that of a baby elephant, became a quasi-involuntary dance, which, given my lack of co-ordination or basic rhythm, just made me look like someone having a seizure.

The laughter had risen to a manic crescendo by the time I reached my spot. Julian, smelling blood, applauded me enthusiastically and said, "Hello Alex. What lovely moves. Are you self-taught?"

Despite this patchy beginning, our presentation went well, and we got a diverse group of enthusiastic young people to whoop and holler with genuine fervour. We finished with a suitably grandiose performance from Clyde Pilestone himself on film. Dressed like a Byronic vampire, my old school friend Nigel stared at the camera and exhorted our people to '*go into that febrile wilderness of the stunted imagination and spread my mad mordant musings to the expectant youth of today's tendentious technological terrain*'. I can honestly say that no one in that room knew what he was talking about.

The day finished with a huge party at a Shoreditch club, with Harvey as DJ, limitless drink and minimalist food to soak it up. I was starving. Every time a tray of miniature designer food appeared from the kitchen, I would pounce as if I'd been told there was an imminent famine. The atmosphere was buoyant, and of course my strange ascent to the stage had now been choreographed into a flash mob routine called 'the Alex'. On an hourly basis, Harvey put on 'Baby Elephant Walk' and every member of the company I had lovingly built would mock me through the medium of dance.

Still, I had never felt so popular. Julian and I were surrounded by a constant flow of people who wanted to introduce themselves or share an idea or suggestion. As exhaustion engulfed me after a long day, compounded by the techno-throb of Harvey's music, conversation became increasingly difficult. I could show no sign of not caring or indifference, so I tried to keep a cheerful fixed grin. I must have looked a bit deranged.

Towards the end of the evening, I was locked in serious debate with Inés from Madrid and Chen from Singapore. The former had a rather impenetrable Latin accent, lubricated by apparently significant quantities of *cerveza*. The latter spoke only in an earnest whisper. I was nodding manically in violent agreement with sentences I did not hear. I think Inés may have said at one point that 'we need strawberry data to wash yesterday's liposuction', although I may have been mistaken. I just wanted to go home and was on the verge of tears when Samantha, our finance director, sidled up and asked if she could have a quiet word. We retreated to the foyer of the club to escape the pounding music.

"I know I'm not allowed to say this, but, Samantha, I will always love you for extricating me from that conversation."

She smiled and took a sip from the wine glass she was holding. "It's been a great day. You should be very happy. We have a great group of people and they all love working here."

"So why the long face? Please don't tell me you've lost the company chequebook?"

"No, it's safe in my handbag, along with the petty cash."

"What is it then?"

"Julian." I knew this was what she was going to say.

"What's he done this time?" I asked, like a fed-up parent enquiring after a naughty child.

"It's his expenses. They are just enormous. I think he's running his life through the business. He's totally cavalier about what he puts on his card."

"Like what?"

"Well, for one thing, last week he bought a bike."

"And?"

"Let's just say, he eats out a lot more than you do. Plus, his wine choices suggest he may well be training to become a sommelier. He's also racked up some hefty travel costs. Did you know he spent a few days at the Cannes Film Festival? I assume he was accompanying his girlfriend, not looking to ask movie stars if they needed anything for their children?"

I felt nauseous, the excessive alcohol not mixing well with the crushing disappointment. I knew this meant imminent confrontation just when it was not needed.

"Why are you telling me this now, at the end of such a long day? Couldn't it have waited until tomorrow?"

"For one thing," she replied with irritation, "it shouldn't matter when I tell you. All that matters is what you do about it. If you must know, he just took me aside and told me to raise the limit on his company credit card, without stopping to explain himself."

I stared at the wall behind her in a state of weary despair. There was a poster with the arresting headline: 'If you feel uncomfortable with someone you meet tonight, ask the barman if Tony is in, and we will have you extricated from a difficult situation.' What a terrible world, where a night out could require such an extreme remedy. I wondered if I should ask for Tony to help me out of this spot.

"I'll think about how to deal with this. We've got the launch in a month. I have to focus on that." Samantha looked disappointed and shook her head.

"I worried you would back out of a fight. Alex, you need to think hard about Julian. The business is about to become incredibly valuable. I'm pretty certain he won't be happy until he's stolen it from you."

She didn't wait for a reply, but headed back to the party. I waited in vain for Tony to arrive and then called an Uber.

17. Consequences

I arrived home at 2 a.m. and Sarah was pacing our bedroom consoling a whimpering Emily, covered in chickenpox and unable to sleep. She had caught it from Theo and Sarah had endured a torrid week, unable to do her surgeries and missing some key training sessions she needed to attend. I tried to do my bit at night, but, as ever, I was a distracted bystander to my own family's small dramas.

"How did you get on?" she asked, sounding exhausted.

"Well, apart from accidently dancing on to the stage and then being mocked by the whole company, I think rather well."

She smiled wanly and for a second was silent as Emily had finally fallen asleep. Deftly, she placed her on our bed and covered her. Emily instinctively stretched her tiny arms and settled into the shape of a star, arms and legs pointing in all directions. There was going to be little room for me, so a few uncomfortable hours in the spare room beckoned.

Feeling quite awake, I said to Sarah, "Do you fancy a quick cup of tea? I'm not ready to sleep. And do you know what, I'm going to go in late tomorrow. To hell with it – I don't have a meeting until 9.15 a.m."

"Oh, that's the crazy rebel I married. Come on, let's go downstairs," she said in a whisper, afraid that my nocturnal burst of energy would undo her hard work getting Emily to sleep. We adjourned to the kitchen and made ourselves a cup of herbal tea. For a second we both stared into space, then I said, "So, how's work?" She looked momentarily confused at a question that I rarely asked.

"How would I know? I've been trapped here with spotty-monster-child from hell."

"I mean when you are actually there, and the patients aren't your offspring."

"Well, since you ask, I do have some news. I got called in a few days ago and offered a partnership in the practice." I sat up with surprise. How could she not mention something so exciting?

"Sarah, that's great. Were you going to tell me at some point?"

"I was if I could ever sit you down long enough to have a conversation. I'm going to say no, and I'm not sure I want to talk about it with you now."

"Why would you do that? It's what you wanted. You are more talented and committed than the rest of them put together. And you can name all the bones in a leg."

She drummed her fingers with irritation and snapped back brusquely, "How can I take on more responsibility? Do you know what a partnership means? Much more admin for a bit more money. There's no way we can function as a family with you constantly absent."

"There is surely a way? There's always a way. We just need to have a plan." I certainly didn't want to block her career progression and suddenly I needed to be constructive and flexible. But it was too late.

"Not with things as they are. I've told them to ask me again in a year. They're going to let me know if they can wait that long for me."

She turned away from me and I knew the conversation was now closed, even though I felt impelled to carry on speaking. Sarah loved the simplicity of being a community doctor, helping people without fuss. She hated not being in charge at a large, badly run practice that she thought she could improve. I had, however, got in the way. After a moment, she smiled once more and changed the subject.

'Is this what a status meeting with you feels like? I've found it very hard to fix one up."

"That's because, I'm afraid, you are not senior enough to warrant much of my precious time."

"Alex, your jokes are not just ill-judged, they are also, unfortunately, quite accurate. I know where I fit in your hierarchy. I'm just hoping someday for a promotion. Now, in the most straightforward way you know how, please just tell me how today went."

I outlined the day, chastened by the realisation that what little time we spent together was often masked by my need to make light of a situation with an uninterrupted barrage of witticisms. I explained the strange sensation of power and influence I'd felt as I realised all these disparate people had been brought together by an ephemeral idea that had come to me because I'd decided to take Theo to the park one sunny day. All day, I had met bright and ambitious individuals looking for their own personal glory. I was expected to be the catalyst.

"And how was Julian today?" she asked. "Did he let you have a go with the microphone? Did all the pretty girls flock to him, not you?" I was silent. My poker face was about as convincing as when Theo would surreptitiously thwack Emily, protesting he hadn't touched her.

"What aren't you telling me, Alex?"

"I uncovered a problem." I couldn't look at her directly. This conversation was going to make me confront what I was trying to avoid.

"Tell me, please," she prompted gently. I inhaled sharply and began.

"Julian is treating the company like his personal bank account at the moment. We have so much money coming in and out that I know he is burying lots of his costs, expecting me not to find out. Actually, thinking about it, he probably doesn't really care. He probably just thinks I'm not strong enough to confront him on it."

"And are you?" she said, stroking my hand.

I didn't know whether to answer the question or thank her for being so supportive. With my customary evasion, I replied, "I'm not sure. When I confront Julian, it will be akin to Germany invading Poland. Global conflict will be the only result."

"You've been practising that line in the taxi home, haven't you?"

"A little, maybe. Look, I know I have to do something about him. It's just we have to launch the book, and make it a success. If I confront him now, everything will unravel. I am going to hatch a plan. I promise."

Sarah was unconvinced as we listened to the stillness of the night, punctuated only by the ticking of our kitchen clock. Suddenly, I felt drained. The exciting coming months were going to be tempered by the sickness embedded in my partnership with Julian. After a few moments, Sarah said quietly, "Do you remember our honeymoon, Alex?"

"Which bit? The lovely hotels, the food or the snogging?"

"No, I mean the accident and what you said afterwards."

She was referring to a horrible incident that had occurred half-way through a beautiful two-week tour of Tuscany. We had been driving our little hire car along some windy country roads after a nasty rain shower. Despite the spray and poor visibility, an aggressive Ferrari driver had tailgated me for a long stretch, and the more I slowed to let him pass, the more frantic and irritated he became. Eventually, as he jerked his car alongside me and began to overtake, we heard the pneumatic brakes and angry horn of a lorry coming towards us. Like a Formula One racer at the first bend, the Ferrari driver completed a tight overtake manoeuvre, but left me braking sharply to allow him to pass. As I did so, our car started to spin helplessly. We pirouetted across the miraculously clear road and hit a tree after several complete spins. The impact broke a light and dented a bumper, and fortunately we emerged unscathed but very shaken.

That night we sedated ourselves with red wine and ate as many desserts as we could, celebrating the continuation of our lives.

I became philosophical and poetic, a lethal combination for someone like me with a predilection for speeches. Sarah was referring to something I said that she teased me for thereafter. Fuelled by a post-wedding surge of love, I proclaimed: 'I will never put us in harm's way again.'

Look, I was young and in love and had just had a great wedding; it made me very sentimental and over-emotional. 'Harm's Way' became a secret code between us whenever we questioned a big decision confronting us. We were simply asking was it right for us, and Sarah was asking me now to protect us all from the harm that could be done by Julian. Especially poignant as she was foregoing promotion to accommodate my ambitions ahead of hers.

"Yes, you're right," I admitted, downing the dregs of my peppermint tea. "I know the road is wet and I am braking hard. Time to learn how to steer in a spin."

"A torturous analogy for 3 a.m. but yes, I think the tree is approaching fast. Now, if you don't mind, I would like to get at least a couple of hours' sleep before morning. Some of us have a proper job, and if I'm too tired, my prescriptions will be even harder to read than normal."

She rose to go up to bed and I called after her, "All that talk of our honeymoon, I'm feeling quite frisky now."

"How exciting for you," she said without turning around, and within a minute she was asleep.

* * *

If Sarah was magnanimous, my father was properly angry, fuelled by an uncomfortable concoction of disappointment and disapproval. These negative emotions had seemed to fester over recent months and the more I tried to make him proud of our achievements, the more dismissive he was of their accomplishment. There were several conflicting factors.

He was intensely critical of me as a father and husband. He adored Sarah, with her vast reserves of tolerance, and really resented the frequency of my absences from everyday family events. 'Even when you do come, you are late, distracted and probably on the phone' was a constant reproach. It was true. I was pretty shambolic at time-keeping, and conference calls tended to start in the office, continue in the cab and conclude in the kitchen. Please don't get the impression that I was not a devoted father. I adored my children and did everything to make them the centre of my existence when I was with them. It was just hard to build a sustained or consistent routine – bath and bedtime were spasmodic events for me.

Mum and Dad had assiduously engaged in all aspects of my life growing up. They immersed themselves in the foibles of my friends, helped with homework and kept abreast of any other challenges I faced. If I was 'third Birnam Wood tree from the left' in the school production of *Macbeth*, they would sit in the front row and tell me my performance was not wooden at all. My friends loved coming round for an intense political debate with my father or to have teen-age anxieties soothed by the wise counsel of my mother.

My father took exception to the elevation of business above my core family responsibilities. For a radical political thinker, he was quite a traditionalist. As I got busier with PrimaParent, his lectures on the balance between the personal and the professional life became more frequent. They were devoted and hands-on grandparents, but every gesture of kindness would be accompanied by a sarcastic little dig: 'I'll be sure to show Emily a picture of you, in case her memory is becoming hazy.'

This anger created an intellectual disregard for what I was achieving. First, I had to contend with Saint Judith, my younger sister, who sacrificed everything for the good of others. She immersed herself in the enormity of running her charity, trying to lessen the horrific

Syrian refugee crisis. As she spent an enormous amount of time on the Turkish/Syrian border, my parents grappled with an uncomfortable mix of pride in her work and fear for her safety. She had become a prominent expert on the crisis, making frequent appearances on television, including one powerful laceration of government inaction on *Newsnight*. She, too, was away from many family events. Her absence was unchallengeable, and we toasted her work with collective admiration.

Our loving relationship was undiminished. I would bore anyone with accounts of her achievements, and she was equally excited about my growing success. I would interrupt everything to have late-night satellite phone calls with Judith in her frozen tent in a desolate refugee camp. She would revel in stories of our growth and particularly wanted all the related celeb gossip, most of which emanated from Julian. I made the unilateral decision that our corporate charity would be Better Futures. We incorporated fundraising effectively on the site and began to attract meaningful donations. My father doubted my altruism. 'Anyone you bring to the site increases its valuation – don't demean us by pretending there's another reason' was a particularly barbed comment I received during one conversation.

Watching his two children diverge in their values evinced a bilious anger. This in turn produced an extreme perspective on tech, outlined in his weekly article in his beloved *Guardian*. His 'High Tech or No Tech' column had given him licence to vent and he developed a cultish following of digital dilettantes who hung on his every critical word.

Our minds, he argued, were disintegrating as our umbilical attachment to phones doomed our children to a lifetime of poor concentration. This self-obsessed landscape catalysed mental fragility, and real relationships and intimacy were being destroyed. His writing was parodic, referring to *Giggle*, *Twotter* and *Instasham*, and

he challenged the start-up world with a section at the end called
'The Needed and the Needless'. It would promote a new business
with a worthwhile social purpose, and pillory another that had no
intrinsic value other than individual wealth creation. His outspoken
Marxist take on entrepreneurialism made him constantly sought
after by media. He was on TV more often than the weatherman.

I should have seen it coming. His frustration with me as a son,
husband and father was evident in every conversation. Still, I assumed,
naively, that if I didn't have his respect, I at least had his loyalty.

* * *

About a week after our global get-together, he snapped. Incensed by
my absence from the family during the chickenpox period, he resented
that my mother had to become a back-up nurse to support Sarah. As
I was scrolling through my early morning emails, sipping my first
coffee of the day, my phone rang. Moshe did not sound happy.

"Tell me, Alex. Do you love your father?"

"Hello, Moshe. I love all my family. And I hope you love yours
too." It was an odd start to the conversation.

"Do you think he loves you?"

"I'm sorry, what's happening here? Why these questions? Are
you upset I've never invited you round for Friday night dinner?"

"Have you read the *Guardian* this morning?" At that moment
I felt suddenly cold and had a foreboding that the strained relationship of recent months was somehow going to find a very
public outlet.

"Can I call you back?" I needed some time to take in what was
clearly going to be criticism in print. Moshe grumpily asked me to
call him without fail as soon as possible. Taking a few deep breaths,
I found the article. Dad had really gone for it. The headline was an
inversion of our principle selling proposition.

WHY PRIMAPARENT.COM DOES NOT MAKE YOU A BETTER PARENT

It then only got worse as my father dismantled my achievements very publicly.

> *Alex Lazarus struggles to make family events. He has two gorgeous children and a saintly wife, who is a brilliant doctor. He is an absent father and a distant husband. He has abandoned the simple pleasures of family life to build a highly valued digital parenting business that attempts to consign the traditional demands of raising children to a basic search for a last-minute birthday present. He will be very rich one day, no doubt, but rich in what? Why does this latest unicorn pretender brand bother me? Surely I should encourage the enterprise of the diligent digital entrepreneur? It causes me, however, sleepless nights and unrelenting mental anguish, because Alex Lazarus, in case you hadn't guessed by our identical surnames, is my son.*

I won't reproduce the rest of the article as it was simply an open letter demanding that I do something else with my life. My father analysed the business and concluded it was yet another way of shirking individual responsibility through the 'cult of instant delivery over effort'. His recurring theme was the irony of me trying to enhance parent/child relationships while becoming a worse father and husband. When I read it, I ran out of the building and walked, directionless, trying to marshal my scrambled thoughts, and I had no intention of calling Moshe back. This was so personal that I didn't care about its corporate impact. After a while my phone rang and I saw my father's number. I felt a strong impulse to throw the phone under the wheels of a passing lorry. Instead, I answered the call, saying nothing.

"Alex, Alex, are you there?" he asked with mounting concern.

"Yes," I replied like a sullen teenager.

"Talk to me, Alex. I know you'll have read it by now. Can we please have a sensible discussion?"

Betrayed and close to tears, I simply said, "Why, Dad? What were you thinking?"

"I had to get through to you."

"You could have just phoned."

"That's all I do. You don't listen. Alex, you are throwing away a life of value for value that has no worth."

"Very clever, Dad," I said, trying to quell my anger and despair. "I know you resent the riches I haven't yet earned."

"I don't mean that," he shouted. "I mean you will look back on this time one day and have no recollection of your children growing up. You may not even have a wife to discuss it with. Your ambition is the mortal enemy of your future well-being."

"That's your opinion. How dare you hurt and humiliate me so publicly? What sort of father does that?" My cheeks were wet by now.

"You'll understand in the future why I had to. I know you will."

"Well, maybe that is when we'll next speak." And with that, the call was over.

18. Success

Clyde Pilestone sat in a futuristic swivel chair as bizarrely imagined galaxy scenes morphed from one vibrant planet surface to the next behind him. Unlike his verbose alter ego Nigel, he was simple and direct as he stared into the camera.

> *"My faithful followers. Thank you for your patience. I am ready to share with you the continuing adventures of Xargon 5, who, you will remember, was left with amnesia and an altered personality on the surface of Neptune. He now has to embark on his journey for redemption even more alone. Needing to be heard across a limitless galaxy, can he be liberated by technology, or will it isolate him further?*
>
> *Find out in my new book… The Galaxy Slayer's Last Stand. Out on September 1st 2015.*
>
> *"And I have reached an important decision.*
>
> *"Our world is in need of change. Like Xargon 5, we have to confront new ways of living. So, I am announcing today that my latest book won't be available in bookshops just yet. If you want to read this next instalment, go to PrimaParent.com/galaxy and you will be told what to do. The first chapter of a new exciting chapter. The future, my friends, is ours to shape."*

The screen dissolved and our web address appeared, ready to conquer the universe. It was that simple. After months of planning with our publishing team and Nigel's hefty entourage, our partnership was launched with a simple film that within a couple of days had been seen across half the globe.

The intensity of the press scrutiny accompanying the announcement was enormous. A number of debates were unleashed by the unusual nature of this publishing deal. Was it the end for printed books? Were conventional businesses to be dismantled by aggressive start-ups? As a civilised society, did we respect success or secretly worship the failure of others?

The primary theme of the book created an interesting narrative of its own. Nigel had, very cleverly, made the isolation of its protagonist, searching for his scattered people across the universe, an analogy for young people scouring social media for meaning but floundering in perpetual isolation. This compelling conversation allowed for wider reflection on the nature of parenting in a disintegrating world of relationships. We hoped the many articles that appeared would communicate that PrimaParent had a laudable purpose to improve family life.

Our PR strategy reflected the dilettantism of Nigel/Clyde. The plan was to not make him available in person, but for him to pop up 'virtually', delighting fans across the globe. Press interviews were beamed on to specially constructed screens in a series of unusual locations. Nigel was filmed in a studio made to look like an arid lunar surface. He kept contextualising the isolation described in the book with the perils of modern existence. The story was basically a galactic social media conversation of a lost individual trying to unravel the whereabouts of his friends. This was further helped by other events we created for his passionate fan base. Every day for a couple of weeks, you could win a chance to have a private conversation with him online. The response was staggering, and Nigel brilliantly played the role of enigmatic and combative philosopher for groups of drooling fans from around the globe.

We were fortunate that the book was the best in the series to date. It combined an undercurrent of contemporary philosophy with a bloody good adventure story. Martian loses family. Martian loses memory and is sad. Martian roams galaxy chasing clues from his communications device. Martian gets a bit of redemption at the end of the book, but not enough to preclude an imminent sequel. The critics loved it and were positive about its unusual distribution. Reviews for *The Galaxy Slayer's Last Stand* were – forgive the pun – out of this world.

> *'Clyde Pilestone's emotional piledriver'*
> *'What we can all learn from a lonely Martian'*
> *'Please Mr Pilestone… make sure this is not your last stand'*

Our spectacular launch party officially heralded our arrival as a substantial business. We hired a club and the finest caterers and mixologists, got a well-known DJ and crammed the place with celebrities of varying levels of obscurity and fame. Julian spent the evening with Lucy pressed to his side. His self-satisfied smile suggested we all laud him for his professional and personal achievements, and a posse of fawning acolytes stood by him, laughing sycophantically. Of course, I wasn't jealous.

I sat in the corner at a table with Nigel, Kate and Sarah, trying to revel in the mood and not worry about making an impression. Sarah was very happy and kept snuggling close to me, holding my hand, her eyes sparkling with pride. Our author, however, got drunk quickly and something in his expression suggested imminent mischief. He chose to grill Sarah on her disappointing choice in men.

"Sarah. You are quite lovely. Was Cupid so cruel as to deliver this *homunculus* as your only soulmate?"

I instinctively felt the need to fight back. "And Kate, I know he's very wealthy now, but don't you feel that you'd be happier with someone who uses shorter words in everyday conversation?"

"Thus speaketh the dullard."

"Honestly, your name is Nigel and you're a thirty-eight-year-old bloke with long hair and an appalling beard, who looks more like a creepy heavy metal fan than a literary genius."

"And Alex, you are thirty-eight and enjoying momentary success because of my genius."

"All right, boys," interceded Kate. "Shall we just leave it for tonight, and you can carry on your playground name-calling when Sarah and I aren't here?"

"I'm not that bothered if you want to go around the back of the club and beat Alex up," Sarah added for good measure. We clinked glasses and toasted our mutual success. I had actually grown to like Nigel, and, beneath the posturing, I think he found me a reliable friend. All he really wanted was for people to be honest with him.

For a moment we stared at the revelry around us and absorbed the energy of the celebration. Dimitri was slow-dancing with Lena, clasping her in his arms as if they were superglued together. The pounding music meant everyone boogied frenetically around them, while they smooched like it was the last dance of the night. Alice was introducing Caroline to people as if she were at a friend's wedding showing off her hot new partner. Moshe and Brooke were at the bar, talking. They were the sole representatives of our investors and were clearly enjoying each other's company. Their knee-touching proximity to one another suggested they did not want to be interrupted. A member of Moshe's security detail stood watchfully a few yards from them, looking for would-be assassins or kidnappers. He blended in as unobtrusively as a dark-suited man-mountain with sunglasses and an earpiece was ever going to.

I had created all this from nothing other than luck, determination and hard work. I resisted a growing desire to make a speech oversharing my emotional excitement. Instead, Julian and Lucy came to join us. I'd chatted to Lucy earlier and got the distinct impression that she thought I was some random colleague of Julian's. I withheld the urge to tell her my life story, but it had been a frustrating reminder that perhaps he and I had different narratives on the growth of the business. Julian pre-empted further introspection by making another toast. We all joined in wearily, having seemingly clinked our glasses every two minutes for the last hour.

"Here's to limitless ambition," he said as Lucy giggled. I'm not sure why, as it wasn't particularly funny. Nigel frowned. He did not adhere to all these self-satisfied declarations. He leant forward and looked at us both.

"So, Julian and Alex. Are you going to thank me? Surely I am the reason you're here tonight. Not your little kiddie website that was going nowhere."

Julian bowed with sarcastic sycophancy. "Nigel, I have a photo of you by my bed. You are the last person I think of before I go to sleep."

"And there I was thinking you just had a big mirror," Kate quipped. I was beginning to enjoy this.

"I have to say that Julian's bedroom is rather disappointingly minimalist," intervened Lucy. She seemed to be missing the point. Julian reflected momentarily and rejoined the fray.

"You can mock me, Nigel. Lord knows, I work with Alex, who doesn't know how to give a straight answer to anything, so I'm used to speaking fluent banter. Actually, I'm loving this celebration and quite frankly I'd be a moron if I didn't acknowledge that we wouldn't be here today without your genius." He had everyone's attention now and his voice was inflamed by both passion and a need to be heard above the throb of the music.

"Can I tell you a very brief story?" Julian asked.

"Only if I can publish it," Nigel retorted. He seemed to be spoiling for confrontation, but Kate gave him a look and he sank further into his chair. Julian waited for a respectful silence before beginning this unexpected soliloquy.

"When my dad went to prison, my life changed. I cried for an hour when he was sentenced. Not because I was sad, but because I was embarrassed. All those early years of trying unsuccessfully to get his attention and suddenly I realised it wasn't worth the effort. I didn't mind that he'd tried to bend the law, but he was clearly not very good at doing so. As an antidote to the shame, I threw myself into tennis. Training five days a week, I would daydream about my winning shots in the final at Wimbledon. Most people who coached me at the time will tell you I didn't make it in the end because I had a terrible temper and the wrong attitude. But I got angry because I knew I wasn't good enough. It frustrated me that I wanted to excel but couldn't.

"My last competitive match was an incredibly tight semi-final, which I lost. It was the furthest I'd ever got in a national competition and I played the best game of my life against a much higher-ranked player. In the end, I lost the tiebreaker when my forehand went down the line, landed millimetres on the wrong side and the umpire called it out. Previously, I'd have tried to maim him with my racket. But the only thing I felt was incredulity at the randomness of it all. If the wind direction had been slightly different, if my racket speed had been altered by the tiniest of fractions, would the rules of physics have carried that ball in? Could it have been different? I decided immediately that my tennis career was over and locked my racket in a cupboard. I didn't want the fickleness of the cosmos to shape my future. I knew I wanted to win more than anything. I would just have to take charge.

"When I said just now that ambition could be limitless, I was talking about us as individuals. If Alex hadn't bumped into Nigel, of course we wouldn't be here. But we wouldn't be mourning the loss of something we didn't know existed. I'd be chasing the next opportunity and expecting it to be successful. Unambitious people want rules and guarantees. I'm successful because I only see what I want and my own path towards its achievement. Nigel, how different are we? Do you actually like children or teenagers, or do you just think they represent the best way to use your writing talent and have the most impact? Your books are successful because you never expected to fail. So yes, of course I'm grateful to you all. But rest assured, I did not give up tennis to fail at something else."

He sat back and took a large gulp of his drink, having ranted for longer than perhaps he had expected. Lucy stroked his arm in approbation of his perfect delivery. No one else spoke. Inevitably, uncomfortable without making a contribution, I looked at Julian and said, "Did you make that all up?"

Ignoring me, he took Lucy's hand and led her to the dance floor.

* * *

The next eighteen months were the making of our business. We released the book in forty-four languages, and it was downloaded nearly twenty-three million times. Remarkably, by making everyone use an e-book reader, we changed behaviour. Kids were now glued even more firmly to their devices, but parents didn't mind because they were reading. We inevitably relented and produced limited print runs of an expensive special edition, which sold out immediately.

We attracted approaches from authors and production companies wanting to shake up established entertainment and publishing practices. PrimaParent rapidly became not just a resource for delivering products and experiences for your children, but also a means of curating their reading and viewing habits. This was a much bigger opportunity commercially than we could have expected.

We brought in a Head of Innovation called Clark Templeton. Recommended most forcibly by the Johnsons, he had enjoyed a succession of ever-upward roles at a variety of Silicon Valley businesses. At the music app bopdewop he had caused an industry stir by signing major artists away from their labels. His remit was to create future growth opportunities by developing new revenue streams. We had to relocate him from the US, paying him the largest salary in the company, which Julian tried, unsuccessfully, to resist. We both agreed that he had a silly name and resented that he was not entirely our choice. I was much more expedient and knew that he represented progress. Julian conversely called him 'Quick Simpleton' as often as he could behind his back.

He was fearsomely bright, having come top in his year at Harvard Business School, and spoke in complex sentences liberally laced with jargon and acronyms. Charming, yes, but he also displayed a detachment in the initial relationships he formed. It was hard to know what he was thinking as his manner was cheery but inscrutable. I wasn't sure if he was impressed by my leadership or reporting my incompetence to our principal investors. Quickly, I grew fearful of his abilities. He had a prodigious work ethic and soon developed compelling new business ideas to broaden our appeal.

We embarked on developing a 'flash sale' children's clothing offering. We would buy brands, unsold or end-of-season inventory, samples, whatever we could get our hands on. Parents loved the deals we secured from major brands, irrespective of whether it was last year's stock. To bolster our fashion credentials further, we persuaded a number of high-profile designers to produce kids' ranges for us. These were limited and very exclusive, not to mention eye-wateringly expensive. (You may remember the furore when the Japanese designer Yota Miyoshi produced babygrows that we sold for £1,000 each.) Our disruptive assault required that we recruit people from major retailers, fashion houses and even ex-editors of glossy magazines. A PrimaParent child was going to be not just entertained but well dressed too.

Clark's other big initiative was the launch of our Expert Division at the end of 2016. Our research showed that while parents loved the breadth of experiences and products available, they also looked to us for guidance. Rather than facilitating chat among enthusiastic laypeople on parenting, we would bring in a panel of experts and make customers pay for the privilege of their guidance. Our proposition was 'It's better to pay for good advice than solicit a lot of unwanted opinion'. Menu pricing allowed access to a panel of medical, behavioural and entertainment experts, to deal with a range of enquiries and produce bespoke PrimaParenting guides for our information-hungry customers.

After four years of trading, we had nearly thirty million global subscribers, annual revenues of £90m, and were even making a small profit, unheard of for a new digital business. We were constantly valued in the press because of the ridiculous noise we had made in our infancy, and speculative valuations suggested we were worth nearly half a billion – that's basically a unicorn without the horn. I owned 19 per cent of the business. I was, on paper, a very rich person.

Virtual wealth does not guarantee happiness and this achievement was built on some shaky relationships and fragile alliances. Remember, the Greeks used three words for ambition and one of them can be translated as 'strife'. That was about to become manifest in the future progression of the company. Our ascent had certainly involved some skirmishes on the way up, but success had come quickly and more easily than I could have expected.

Not for much longer.

19. Attack

I couldn't get in the lobby of our office because of all the demonstrating clowns.

There were perhaps two hundred of them defying the snapping cold of a January morning, and they were angry, even with the enormous smiles painted garishly on their faces. They carried placards that read 'Poo PrimaParent' and 'Toot your horn if you hate PrimaParent'. A barrage of custard pies was lobbed at anyone foolish enough to cross their makeshift picket line. It had all been an innocent misunderstanding and The Global Federation of Clowns had lost their legendary sense of humour, simply because of a slightly misjudged advertising campaign.

Frank and Frankie had joined us full-time in 2016 as our in-house creative directors, building a team of fertile minds ambitious about producing talked-about ideas to support our increasing fame. One morning, the husband-and-wife team dragged me into a conference room to show me a visual, with the excitement of sugar-fuelled children opening presents on Christmas Day.

It was certainly arresting. They had mocked it up very realistically by shooting it with their team all dressed as clowns. The image showed five of them standing disconsolately, reading the paper or scrolling through their phone, clearly with nothing very much to do. The headline stated 'Who needs Clowns?' and the subhead explained: 'There's more to PrimaParent than you think. Take your kids a bit more seriously.'

"It's quite aggressive to clowns," I observed. "We have loads of them registered, don't we? I'm not sure we should be attacking them in public. We might upset them, and no one likes to see 'the tears of a clown'." Ignoring my feeble humour, they mounted a well-prepared case for why the art of clowning was rapidly dying out. There was significant evidence proving that children were now afraid of the murderous appearance of traditional clowns. Entertaining kids these days required a better look.

We debated the ad for some time. Alice was all for it, believing that clowns were symbols of the 'entertainment patriarchy'. Julian hated clowns too, associating them with unhappy trips to the circus with grandparents attempting to cheer him and his sister up while their father was in prison. Clark, our newest addition, was entirely rational and felt that the 'data suggested a brand net gain'. Only the brooding and increasingly dark Dimitri, who rarely commented on marketing, had a curious loyalty to them. He cited some ancient Ukrainian folklore that suggested if you cross a clown you will meet with misfortune or, at the very least, a nasty rash. In the end, the overwhelming consensus was that we needed always to be challenging, even if we lost a few sellers along the way. We were rather brazen about the risk of reputational damage.

The campaign ran with considerable investment from us, the first conventional advertising we had ever attempted. For a few days, we got favourable and amused comments. Then an extremely disgruntled deputation from the aforementioned Global Federation of Clowns arrived at our offices. Their commitment to the cause was such that they arrived in full clown regalia. I found myself in the unexpected position of sitting with Alice in a meeting room with four people dressed like Ronald McDonald. Resisting the urge to order a Happy Meal, we listened intently to their anger and agreed to think about it and respond.

The campaign was due to end ten days later, so rather than lose money pulling it, we told them that when it was over, we would not run it again. (We had no intention of doing so anyway and were already working out the next minority group we could offend with the follow-up.) Sadly, hell hath no fury like a pissed-off clown, and this was not acceptable to them. They decided to demonstrate as often as they could outside our offices. Since none of them could find much work as a clown, this turned out to be weekly.

At first, it was distracting but not problematic. It garnered a lot of publicity and the prevailing view was that clowns were contradictory, as children could not be entertained by a character they found frightening. Then the demonstrations got angrier and more disruptive. A discernible shift in public opinion suggested we were acting like corporate bullies. When an article appeared in the business pages of a Sunday paper claiming that 'PrimaParent is exhibiting the tantrums of a spoilt child', we knew it was time to act.

On that January morning, I asked the GFC's executive director, who used the *nom de guerre* 'Lovable Giggles' but was really called Roger, to join us in our office. We apologised to him, handed over a sizeable donation to their benevolent fund and agreed to eat humble custard pie by printing a retraction ad. A couple of weeks later, we took out a full-page in *The Times* with the headline: 'This is what happens to naughty boys and girls'. The visual was seven clowns with custard pies in their faces. Excruciatingly, we knew we had to appear in our own ad to show some contrition. I made sure I stood at the back and was unrecognisable under my orange wig.

The 'Clown Wars' were a sobering but ultimately useful experience. We turned opinion back in our favour, and there was a positive correlation between any news story and engagement with our site. It also showed that we were now no longer a scrappy start-up looking for fame at all costs. Everything from now on was a fight to preserve our reputation and behave with integrity rather than opportunism.

* * *

Our love of PR always got us extra scrutiny from journalists and bloggers looking to halt our progress. There were several examples of our vulnerability.

A few months before the clowns, we had to weather a drugs bust. One morning, the lift doors opened and a battalion of uniformed police emerged, to the confusion of our half-awake workforce. I was quickly called to talk to DCI Helen Mason, who asked me to take her to two developers, Jan and Michael. Being something of a coward, I was completely intimidated by the arrival of law enforcement officers, who were all much taller than me, and led them meekly to the two individuals. Ashen-faced, they frantically tried to do something to their computers and were immediately arrested.

It turns out they were running an amphetamine and ecstasy distribution business from our offices. Using the dark web and our servers, they controlled a network of East London couriers responding to orders. We never saw them again, but the investigation was time-consuming as an angry and shocked Dimitri had to help the police unravel what had happened. Jan and Michael had been popular and engaging members of the team, without attracting attention to their side business. Dimitri took the betrayal very badly and it made him angrily question his control of the people who worked for him. We obviously hoped to keep the story out of the news. Not so the police, who were eager to showcase how they had uncovered a multi-million-pound drugs business outsmarting the technical wizardry of an arrogant start-up. They couldn't wait to host a press conference, and we found ourselves defending our integrity from news stories that revelled in headlines like this:

DRUGS FACTORY ASSEMBLED IN PARENTING
WEBSITE... AND THEY WEREN'T USING LEGO

Our corporate self-defence went into overdrive and there were a number of consequences. We had to ensure a code of behaviour among our young staff based on zero tolerance of any drugs-related misdemeanours. On the orders of Brooke and Cole, we reluctantly introduced random drug-testing, which we hated. Overnight we went from being liberal and tolerant to an unforgiving workplace with a rigid code of conduct.

Moshe had little concern for the physical well-being of our staff but was truly horrified that there had been such a dramatic breach of security protocols. He sent his beloved Avi Ram with a small team to review our systems and to introduce some bespoke protection. Dimitri was incandescent and insulted by this intrusion, doing everything possible to be unhelpful. We had to intercede at one point to prevent him taking a hammer and smashing the laptops of the exuberant Israelis ordering him around. When they left, he became like an insecure dictator afraid that power was slipping away and imposed the equivalent of IT martial law on his team. They could not get a glass of water from the kitchen without his consent. It would be fair to say that he was no longer considered an inspirational team leader.

We sensed a divine power resented our success, because it was one bad story after another. Some weeks later, I received a call from a journalist who gleefully asked me to comment on the situation with 'Threads for Teds'. I didn't know what he was talking about, so he emailed me the article he was writing, giving me almost no time to digest its implications before calling me back.

Teddy bears were always in need of decent clobber, often arriving at their new home in nothing more than a flimsy scarf. 'Threads for Teds' was the solution to that problem, offering a host of costume choices. Now they could be dressed as Construction Worker Teddy, Cowboy Teddy or Biker Teddy en route to the YMCA. They even had a bespoke made-to-measure range. The ambitious start-up prospered with us, particularly due to our international expansion. Americans loved fancy-dress soft toys, it seemed.

Unfortunately, our teddies were being kitted out courtesy of ten-year-old children in several well-hidden factories in Myanmar. The horrific story was made worse by allegations that they were being kidnapped from their families. UNICEF was leading an international investigation with a thorough examination of their supply chain. To make matters worse, their success, for which, as a major channel of distribution, we were partly responsible, meant the evil factories could be linked back to us.

The journalist relished my discomfort at this revelation. Pushed for a comment, I spluttered something spontaneous about being horrified, shocked and angry and said I would lead a major investigation into our vetting procedures. Unfortunately, I did not do the most obvious thing and sever our commercial relationship. The next day a headline appeared, decrying our hypocrisy:

PRIMAPARENT: PROFITS
BEFORE CHILDREN

Alice had to instigate a huge review of our sellers, introducing new terms of business conduct that took great effort to implement throughout our global organisation. It also became an open season for critics to undermine the rapidity of our growth, highlighting a lack of ethical behaviour.

We built a big PR team to deal with daily negative stories, using Twitter extensively to bolster our response when under attack. Naively, I had assumed success would mean days spent with feet up on the desk, chomping on a fat cigar. Little did I imagine I would be grappling continuously with endless complaints from disgruntled parents around the world about children's parties that had gone wrong. (*Imagine little Sven's disappointment when the piñata we ordered proved indestructible.*)

We were attacked for promoting books with dubious moral content, and criticised for not having a view on Brexit, failing to endorse Trump, having a Jewish founder, and selling designer dresses to under-tens. The more famous we became, the more an unseen global chorus of criticism would come our way. If our PR team grew fast, our legal team grew even faster. Julian hired Charles Tomlinson from Disney as chief counsel. Charles was a bundle of neurotic energy. He trusted no one, was volatile and prone to bouts of unexpected anger. His desk was covered in mounds of randomly assorted paper and his coffee consumption was prodigious. The giant sweat patches under his arms would spread like a rancid oil slick during the course of a stressful day. He was perfect.

Commercial contracts and litigation started to flow freely. First, we had publishing, distribution and talent deals to sort out. We also had to ensure that our seller arrangements were watertight and internationalised as we spread across territories. If a product was late, if a service did not live up to its description or if a download didn't work, we were threatened with some form of legal action. Most of it was fairly harmless stuff – amateur attempts to win compensation, often through the indiscriminate use of Latin. You know the sort of stuff. We were threatened with a bit of *habeas corpus* because we failed to use *lingua franca* and were caught *in flagrante delicto.*

More seriously, our tech swagger made us enemies. We found ourselves on the receiving end of politicians trying to make a name for themselves. In Oregon, State Senator Hamilton Jones Jnr moved to stop our digital downloads, claiming they infringed an arcane bookseller tax. The financial penalty was minimal, but spotting the opportunity for fame, he created a narrative that played well across large swathes of the country. We were positioned as killers of the physical book, destroyers of family life across the great nation.

Initially, we thought it all a bit of a joke, but soon realised that there was considerable sympathy for his position infecting the conservative Midwest. We had to demonstrate in court that the law was out of date and irrelevant, as well as an excessively punitive restriction of our ability to trade. Our response was extensive. One day, I gave twenty interviews from a small booth in Central London to local TV stations across the country, from St Louis to Oregon. I spoke to Kendall, Jeff, Courtney, Madison, Kelly-Anne and Kelly-Kate, and a host of other perky presenters. They all asked if I slept comfortably, knowing that children across the US were having their childhoods destroyed by having to read popular books on a phone. Sweaty and tenacious Charles prevailed in this instance and we carried on, bruised and a little more vulnerable.

Disputes kept arising like those little jumping plastic frogs you hit with a hammer in the fairground. Push one down and another one popped up. In Germany, we got into a bitter wrangle with a copycat site, *firstparent.com*, which basically cloned our original seller/experience marketplace. It turned out that a disgruntled German engineer who had worked for us was the culprit. Tired of being bullied by Dimitri, he returned to Berlin, secured backing from a tenacious partner, and downloaded all the information he had stolen while at PrimaParent to build a basic carbon copy of our business. The EU 'passing off' competition law was opaque and courts in Germany were hostile to a British tech business. Call it hubris, but we could do very little other than be confident that our publishing and entertainment strength made us a much more popular destination.

Charles was an adept general, able to fight battles on simultaneous fronts. But lengthy conflict stretched our resources significantly, blurring our operational focus. We were by now noisily famous, having disrupted so many established sectors globally. Everyone wanted to pick a fight with us, and conflict was unavoidable. The real battle, though, was about to begin, and it was going to be much more personal.

20. This Means War

My phone pinged loudly next to my bed at 5 a.m. and I awoke from a deep sleep, disoriented. Sarah, mercifully, had her back to me and carried on slumbering, emitting the occasional tuneful lady-snore. I focused groggily on the screen and saw the message was from Moshe and extremely brief: *Meet me at my suite. 7.45 a.m.*

I had no idea he was in town nor where he was staying, but assumed it would be his favourite white palace at the St Martins Lane Hotel. Slightly unnerved, I lay staring at the ceiling, wondering instinctively why I was in trouble. A couple of hours later, I said good morning to the security detail standing outside his suite and, to my surprise, the door was opened by a shoeless Brooke, who gave me an unenthusiastic kiss on each cheek as she fiddled with putting on an earring.

Moshe was at the dining room table reading the *FT* and drinking black coffee, a modest bowl of fruit salad next to his cup. I went to shake his hand and was slightly overwhelmed once again by his pungent and liberally applied cologne, probably called something like 'Eau de Succes'. Brooke joined him at the table and poured us both some coffee. There were no minders or flunkies – it was the oddest domestic set-up, and I wondered what was going on. If I looked in any way quizzical, they did not seem to notice or care. Moshe wiped his lips fastidiously on a napkin, stared at me for a nervous moment and then said simply: "You have to fire Julian."

The silence was punctuated sharply by the sound of Brooke's knife cutting an apple in half with an executioner's zeal.

"Why?" I asked, not entirely surprised.

"Why do you think?" This was one of those tests from Brooke I knew I had to pass. I just wasn't sure of the answer. I had no intention of defending Julian and wondered if I now had the opportunity to precipitate his demise.

"Hasn't he paid back his loan? Are his expenses completely out of hand? Is he more concerned with his own PR agenda? Or has he finally admitted that he actually doesn't like children? You tell me."

Moshe looked stern, his default expression. "These are side issues you should have been on top of anyway. Alex, please remind me of the share ownership of this business."

"Julian and I have just under 19 per cent each. The team and staff a further 10 per cent. You both have 15 per cent, as does George. The rest is in the hands of the other investors, like iSeed. But you know all this, Moshe, it's not exactly a secret. Where is this going?"

"We are moving in a direction that requires you to pay close attention, or you'll find yourself with much more time at home with the kids."

Moshe hardly looked up as Brooke went to the desk in the corner of the room and returned with a single sheet of paper. "You had better see this. Read it carefully and think before you reply."

I grabbed the paper a little too forcefully and saw that it was an email from Julian, addressed to George and Cole. Headed 'Alex', it was less than twenty-four hours old.

Gentlemen. We need to talk immediately.

I am convinced that we need to change the leadership of the organisation. Alex has lost the respect of the entire team. He is unfocused, indecisive and incapable of making strategic or difficult decisions. There is a real danger he will jeopardise our future ability to drive new publishing arrangements for Clyde

Pilestone content. I would like to discuss removing him from the business and restructuring it around my leadership with the support of the current team, who will no doubt be relieved by such an outcome. Please can we convene immediately to discuss a plan that I can quickly execute.

My heart began its traditional panicky rumba, but I was also overcome by quiet fury. How dare he lie so blatantly to oust me from my business. It was *my* idea and the product of *my* relentless determination. Most certainly not his.

"Why is this note only to George and Cole?"

"Alex, you are very naive. He is canvassing support. When he gets those two on board, he expects that Cole will be able to persuade me. Then Moshe will be less of a problem."

Moshe, who had been conducting this conversation while pretending to scan the newspaper, now looked up. Honestly, it was like he was following a set of stage directions to enhance his macho persona or auditioning to be the next James Bond villain.

"But I am a problem. You see, I have never liked Julian. I know who has the drive and integrity. You do. I am troubled, however, by one nagging thought."

"And that is?"

"Are you really good enough? Is it worth the effort to support you? There are lots of very talented CEOs out there, aren't there, Brooke."

"So many great CEOs, Moshe. Not enough companies worthy of their talents."

"Founders come up with great ideas and make them happen. They just might not be the best people to run with them," Moshe added, in case I hadn't realised that my future was being questioned through a series of business clichés. I was properly irritated by now and their posturing was not going to intimidate me.

"What is going on here? You're telling me I'm under threat and threatening me at the same time. Strange motivational tactic. You have presented me with a very clear set of options. Attack or be attacked by Mr Smooth, my so-called partner. Well, if it's a war he wants, fine. I am not going to lose everything to an amoral chancer." I glanced at Moshe and, to emphasise the point, added, "Besides, if you go into battle, you always want the Israelis on your side."

"Very amusing," said Brooke, without smiling. Moshe poured himself another coffee and stared out of the window.

"What worries me much more," I continued, "is the sniping and lack of faith you have in me. I think I've done enough to earn your respect. If you want me out, do your worst, because I am going nowhere." I was shouting and gesticulating furiously by now, as if directing traffic at rush hour.

"Calm down, Alex. You will have a seizure and you are much better to us alive and well. We need a strong CEO more than ever." Moshe seemed to have softened and Brooke leant forward and touched my arm in an unexpectedly maternal fashion. In fact, she gave it a little squeeze.

"We back you, Alex. We just needed to see that you are brave enough for the ensuing unpleasantness."

"*Unpleasant* is my middle name. Well, it's Leon actually." The nervous joke fell out unnecessarily, but Moshe carried on, oblivious to my ill-judged attempts at humour.

"Get control of the board immediately. If you control the votes, you can get rid of Julian. Have a plan and execute it quickly. You seem to like a bit of Israeli military history. Remember the Six Day War?" I nodded obediently. It was one of my favourite wars. "We pre-empted a long campaign by destroying the Egyptian air force before any fighting had begun. One morning we attacked, because they weren't ready. All their planes and runways in one go. You need to do the same. Early one morning, attack first and attack unexpectedly."

"I get the point, General. I'll get some legal advice and I'm sure that soliciting support from the other shareholders won't be a problem."

"You need to think carefully, Alex, and work out how to put the knife in and twist quickly." Brooke was expressionless, although suddenly she had apparently turned into Lady Macbeth. The conversation oscillated between the language of military strategy and how to plan a murder. They were a curious team, Brooke and Moshe. Charismatic individuals with a capacity for warmth, but driven by a resolve and commercial determination that excised the need for unnecessary emotional distraction. They expected the same from me. I was beginning to uncoil, feeling excited that it was time to part company with Julian. I really didn't like him much and he was making my life unnecessarily miserable.

"May I ask you both a question?"

"What now?" said Moshe, clearly impatient that I was prolonging the conversation instead of popping out to get my axe sharpened.

"Why are you two plotting together? What's happened to Cole in all of this?"

Moshe tutted dismissively. "All you need to understand for now is that Brooke and I are a team, together in a way that she is not with Cole."

That, of course, didn't explain anything. My encounters with Moshe were not always so tetchy, though his dislike of being challenged was consistent, as well as his perpetual need to maintain enigmatic control. He didn't want you ever to understand his motivations fully. Brooke jumped in with an equally unconvincing explanation.

"We are simply protecting our investment, which means we are protecting you. Cole and I see things rather differently at the moment." I wondered if a shoeless Cole was breakfasting in a hotel with George Dobson as we spoke. Somehow unlikely.

Moshe got up, walked to the window and did a series of stretches for the exertions of the day ahead. "I don't trust Julian with my money. I do not trust his godfather, George Dobson. And I most certainly don't trust her husband."

"And you trust me? That's the nicest thing you've said in ages." Moshe actually smiled, although I wasn't sure if it was at my assumption that maybe he actually liked me.

"I trust *you* to have the support of the staff, not Julian. That's the main reason we are here. Now if you don't mind, can we change the subject and start doing some work."

The pleasantries were over, although nothing had felt that pleasant.

* * *

I don't know why I missed so many signs. Perhaps I was too busy or afraid of confrontation. Or maybe just a bit naive, believing that, however fractious the relationship, human decency would prevail.

About ten days previously, Julian and I had gone out for a rare lunch. A cancelled appointment had left me with unexpected free time and Julian was mooching round the office chatting to people indiscriminately. I would often watch him adopt the role of a minor royal visiting the factory floor. He would approach random individuals, hands clasped behind his back, bend down benevolently and engage them in conversation. They would always dissolve into bouts of infectious laughter. I'm sure all he'd said to them was 'who are you and what do you do?' but it seemed to work. He was far more absent in the office these days but seemingly took corporate morale very seriously.

I don't know what made me want to catch up with him – probably fear that I didn't really know what he was thinking any more. He

seemed genuinely delighted at my invitation, which I found unsettling as he rarely sought my company.

We adjourned to one of the many new restaurants of King's
Cross. Bustling and energetic, it reflected the ambition of the working people it fed. No longer just a place for lunch, there were start-up
meetings going on everywhere – tables laden with laptops, coffee
cups, and very little food. Most challengingly, if you did eat, you
needed a glossary of obscure pulses, seeds and vegetables to tackle the
menu with confidence. I was starving and the choice between 'mung
choi', 'chermoula', 'mung bean' and 'scamorza' was not making
things any easier.

Julian was contemplative. His divorce from Catherine was
imminent but there was very little remorse or sentimentality, nor
concern for his children growing up in two homes. He was bliss-
fully happy with Lucy and his embryonic celebrity status as her
partner. Profiles of this talented power couple, bright and brilliant,
were everywhere. He confided that their engagement was inevitable but needed to be built around her busy movie schedule and a
planned Broadway run as Hedda Gabler the following year. What
was causing him untold frustration, however, was the financial
settlement he was being forced to agree. Catherine's hurt and anger
manifested in an unflinching determination for adequate compensation for her pain. Sarah and I had bumped into her one Sunday a
few months previously in a local restaurant and I found her warm
and friendly, quite a different person to the sad and angry victim of
Julian's solipsism.

She was genuinely excited for the success of PrimaParent and
had recently moved consultancy firms, loving her new role. It felt a
little strange discussing Julian's business with her, and she did ask me
some quite specific questions about the rate of our growth, which I
answered, I thought, innocently. Her last words before she returned

to her table were enigmatic. She had given me a hug, which she held on to for a second longer than I had expected. Lowering her voice, she said cheerfully, 'Keep up the hard work, Alex. Your success is my success.'

At lunch, Julian went into enormous detail about the fractious negotiations that had taken place between their respective lawyers. The issue of maintenance and property had been relatively uncontested. More problematic was the division of the potential value of PrimaParent. Catherine wanted her share. There were two issues: the amount she was due and the valuation of the company. Julian talked openly with me about the legal arguments being used by both sides. I felt the need to show him solidarity for no other reason than we seemed to be getting on so well. I thought he'd be interested in my recent encounter with Catherine.

"Did I tell you, Sarah and I bumped into her recently?"

Julian put his cutlery down and stared at me with a mixture of curiosity and concern. "What did you talk about?"

"Oh, you know, kids, the weather, the ideal Spurs formation. Nothing too serious."

"Did she ask about the business?" This was feeling uncomfortable. I had wondered why she was fixating on the number of new offices we were opening.

"She might have done in passing, I can't really remember."

Unconvinced by my evasiveness, Julian pressed for an answer. "Yes or no?"

"She did." I felt I was in court now myself and nearly called him 'Your Honour'.

"What did she ask specifically?"

"Just how we were doing." I couldn't have sounded that convincing by now, and inscrutability is a facial expression I have yet to master.

"Catherine has one of the cleverest business minds I know. She doesn't ask vague questions. Did she want to know how we were growing globally?"

"Yes, it was something like that. Julian, it was weeks ago, and it was a short conversation. I can't really vouch for what I specifically said."

"All right, let me ask the question slightly differently. Is it feasible you mentioned that we were about to open in five more countries, including Japan?"

"Look, it wasn't like I gave a formal presentation of our business plan. Maybe I said something like 'things are good, we're really busy conquering the world'. I can't be sure." By now I had a rather scary recollection of my surprise when she asked directly if we were going to open in Tokyo. Wanting always to sound impressive, I had proudly told her of my imminent trip to do just that. The game was up, and stuttering half-truths to assuage Julian's rising frustration seemed pointless.

"I think I did tell her I was off to Japan. What could have possibly been wrong with that? It was hardly a secret in the business."

"Oh, Alex, what have you done?" He leant back in his chair, shaking his head.

"What is going on here? I just had a casual chat with her. These are not state secrets."

"Maybe not, but the picture I'd painted to her lawyers was slightly different. I needed them to think that progress was slowing down a bit and we were holding off significant new markets. It's pretty obvious that Japan is going to be very important to us and I couldn't understand how they managed to change their line of attack. It felt like they had an inside track but it never occurred to me that your bumbling big mouth would cost me so much money. The valuation went up significantly after you blabbed."

"That can't be true. Honestly, you're reading too much into a casual encounter." I refused to believe that I had unwittingly been embroiled in their divorce. Julian, however, did not want to discuss anything further, nor contemplate an alternative to the views he had formed. We sat in a portentous and extremely unsettling silence as the plates were cleared by the waitress.

Julian eventually looked at me with contempt and growled: "Can you settle up? I have to make a phone call." He didn't wait for an answer as he headed to the door.

* * *

A few days after my meeting with Moshe and Brooke, Sarah told me she was pregnant.

It was a lovely moment – what else could it be? We had always planned a third, and as Theo and Emily were now six and four, they were practically independent adults. My children were my finest accomplishment, way beyond a digital business now worth hundreds of millions. If I spent more time and energy at work, it was only because I wanted to build a good future for them. That's what I told myself on long-haul plane trips on a Sunday night or weeks filled with sixteen-hour days and no contact with them whatsoever.

We celebrated our happy family news with some takeaway sushi. The kids were asleep and the house calm, cosy and suburban. I had not really been home too much that week, so I filled her in on my conversation about Julian. By then, the penny had dropped that my supposed indiscretion with Catherine may have fuelled the coup he was planning.

"I don't want to tell you I told you so," Sarah said while adeptly picking up some tuna sashimi with her chopsticks.

"Well then, don't say anything," I replied.

"Like that's going to stop me. I mean, what did you want me to do? Get a 'Julian will betray you' tattoo? I really hope this next child doesn't inherit your emotional intelligence."

"Maybe they can check for that at the scan?"

"What are you going to do?"

"Well, I'll love the child even if he or she turns out a worse judge of character than me."

"That's a relief. Answer the question, please."

"I am going to strike first."

"And what if it becomes truly horrible? Have you got the stomach for the fight?"

I instinctively patted my tubby gut. Exercise was an infrequent endeavour for me. "Yes, I have enough stomach for any battle. Look, I'm not giving up my control of the business until I'm ready. Don't you think I knew this day would come? I've just always put it to the back of my mind and tried to concentrate on business, hoping he'd go away before the problem blew up. I got that wrong. I'm a bit sick of everyone thinking I haven't got the balls for running a business this big."

I got animated and was almost shouting by now. Sarah patted her stomach like I had just done and put a finger to her lips. "Shhh, you'll wake the new baby." What further was there to discuss? I was going to visit a lawyer to wage war on Julian. Unfortunately, there was an outstanding matter, which I knew she would bring up.

"How are we going to tell your parents? Perhaps this can be the cause of a truce with your father?" I may have omitted in this narrative the update that after my father's assault on me in the press, we too had been at war. We hadn't spoken.

Despite frequent entreaties from the women in my life – mother, wife, sister – I refused to see him. There had been little in the way of apology from either party. I met my mother for awkward lunches in which her palpable pain was not enough to prompt a reconciliation. My sister was sympathetic to my outrage at the article but would relentlessly implore me to be the bigger person and forgive him. Sarah was still a regular visitor to their house and made sure the children did not suffer as a consequence of the truculent pride of their father and grandfather.

I knew Dad was suffering, which perhaps gave me sadistic pleasure. So when Sarah brought up the subject of sharing the good news with my emotionally vulnerable parents, I chose to ignore the possibility of rapprochement, still angry with him for publicly invalidating my success. I was just not ready to concede his argument that I had sacrificed a bit of my soul for the ambition ride.

"Sarah. It's going to have to wait. I'm on the eve of battle here. I can only focus on one upset at a time. You tell them for me." With that, the evening's celebrations brusquely ended and I started to clear the plates away.

21. Law and Peace

For a few days, Julian and I co-existed in a state of artificial cordiality. I cancelled a couple of scheduled European trips to fledgling offices and we fluttered around the office, nodding politely to one another, or sat in meetings with lots of other people, behaving impeccably. Outwardly, we co-parented our company like the happiest mum and dad in the world. Behind the scenes, I was preparing an underground stockpile of arms to blow things up spectacularly. The legal advice was clear: this was going to be a popularity vote in the boardroom. If I had support amounting to over 50 per cent of the share ownership, I could dismiss him. He could keep his shares, but he would no longer be a director. The corporate equivalent of a Mafia bullet through the head.

Winning control was basic maths. Julian and I owned the same amount of the business. I could count on Moshe and Brooke and he had George and Cole on his side. Honours even. iSeed, represented by Jane Thomas, had 4 per cent. Dimitri and Alice had a further 2.5 per cent. Samantha, our finance director, had 1 per cent, and 4 per cent was split among the senior leadership team globally. Some smaller investors introduced by Cole and Brooke had the remaining few per cent.

I was sure Dimitri, Alice and Samantha would side with me. I had hired them, and they understood my dedication to the business. I was not close to Jane and regretted not having cultivated a relationship, given she had lunched with Julian several times over the years. Surely this would not be problematic as she was always measured in her approach and had been incredibly complimentary when I'd secured the Clyde Pilestone deal. There was a slight snag in that George was our chairman. The idea had been to rotate the chair between George and Moshe, or at the very least give it a bit of a swivel. But when the time to swap had arisen after a couple of years, Moshe announced that he was relaxed about George carrying on in perpetuity. This meant that George could have a casting vote in the event of deadlock. Even so, I was confident that Julian would struggle to beat me in the likeability stakes.

The word 'covert' has rarely been used to describe someone as innately indiscreet as me. In this case, my compulsion to overshare had to be resisted. I had to recruit my allies without evincing suspicion from Julian and, according to my lawyers, convene the board meeting within a week.

My strategy was therefore to have a conversation with the other shareholders, trust them to back me and then ambush Julian. Starting with Jane, I left a message and awaited a reply, which did not come in the first twenty-four hours of manoeuvres. I adjourned to a coffee shop at the other end of King's Cross and, secreted between a pot plant and a coat stand, phoned Alice, Dimitri and Samantha, asking them to meet me in turn and not tell anyone.

The first conversation with Alice was heart-warming. I was on sure footing because as soon as I had outlined the unfolding scenario, she gave me a bear-like hug for an inordinate amount of time. After a while, I felt the rise and fall of her shoulders and the tears on her face, pressed inappropriately close to mine.

"Please let go, Alice. I said we needed to be subtle. Everyone will think I've just proposed and will start congratulating us."

"Oh Alex, let me enjoy the moment. This is really good news."

"Fine, but I have to speak to Dimitri and Samantha, so I'd rather not draw attention to myself."

"It's just that I'm extremely relieved. We'll all be so much better off without Julian."

"He hasn't gone anywhere yet. Let's not pre-empt our success."

"You can't lose a popularity contest with Julian. It would be as likely as Sarah leaving you for a serial killer."

"Lovely thought. I hope you're right."

"I know I'm right. We've built a great business and you should be very proud. Julian of course has made a significant contribution, but only when it's suited him."

"It's nice of you to say so."

"What else did you think I'd say? You had me at 'hello'."

We talked a bit about how to approach Nigel and Kate, our most important partners. I knew they had no loyalty to Julian but, equally, I needed to take them into my confidence to avoid them worrying about committing further to a business with an unresolved civil war.

After she had left, I waited forty-five minutes before calling Dimitri. I knew he was going to be unemotional and unpredictable. He was by now a malevolent influence in the business – hard, harsh and hurtful. He had many nicknames among his team, miraculously kept from him. 'The Evil Czar' was my personal favourite. Dimitri eventually arrived, emanating a froideur that was positively Siberian.

"Alex, why are you calling me out at such an inconvenient time? Do you have a terminal illness? I can't think of another reason for such urgency."

"No, I'm well, thank you, and I hope that's not a disappointment."

"Well, what then? Have you sold the company without telling us?"

"I need to discuss Julian with you." I sensed him tense a little, which surprised me. He performed an elaborate bottom-shuffle on the leather sofa.

"What about him?"

"Dimitri, you know how much I trust you and respect you."

He did not respond directly, but gave a diffident shrug, impervious to such brazen compliments. I pushed on.

"You are going to need to choose between us."

"Choose what?"

"Who you want to run the company. Julian wants me out. I don't know why, but I'm not going to let this happen."

He remained silent, biting his lower lip with his eyes focused elsewhere.

"This company was my idea. I brought in the content that has created its true value. And I care about its people. That's why I have to stay."

"I understand, but I have to tell you, Julian is stronger and braver. You worry about upsetting people. He doesn't worry about anything or anyone."

"Well, in a few days' time I have every intention of upsetting him significantly and I need your complete support. Given I brought you into this adventure, I assumed this would not be an issue."

"So, you are asking me to make an interesting choice between loyalty to you or the company? It is not necessarily the same thing."

I was trying to stay calm, but this was proving more taxing than I had expected. Since he had arrived as an awkward twenty-year-old in London, I had looked out for him and tried to give him guidance in the basic rules of social interaction. I may have benefited from his brilliance, but I stood up for him when his coldness alienated the people around him. Was it too much to expect that he could stand up for me when required? Clearly it was, because the stubborn bastard was refusing to make this easy.

I found myself spelling out the case for my defence like I was in a courtroom drama. I summarised achievements and cited my positive character traits. Dimitri nodded a lot and occasionally made the odd laconic comment like 'that's your opinion' or 'there is evidence that disproves this'. As ever, when cornered, my voice grew squeaky and less assertive.

Eventually, I knew it was time to sum up and await the verdict of this most emotionless judge. Nothing was forthcoming. Instead, after pressing him for the last time for a decision in my favour, he simply said: "Alex. I will take everything you say into consideration and when the time comes, my decision will be the right one. I will say no more to anyone and now I think I should leave."

He got up and strode to the door without looking back, leaving me feeling angry and extremely nervous. I had expected this conversation to be a formality. But he had made it clear his voting intentions lay elsewhere, thereby cancelling out Alice's previous enthusiastic backing.

I was still confident that fairness and decency would prevail, reinforced by my brief conversation with Samantha, our smallest shareholder. She didn't go for the big hug like Alice, but high-fived me and simply said, "What took you so long?" We didn't need a lengthy discussion, but she agreed to help me with anything required in terms of ammunition or paper trails that could discredit Julian further, particularly his expenses, which, she informed me, were now 'truly astonishing at times in their inappropriateness'.

Rather than returning to the office, I went for a walk to clear my head and evaluate how my campaign was going. I desperately needed to speak to Jane at iSeed, who had not replied to two phone calls. Unsettled, I decided to change strategy and go see her in person. Her assistant told me that she was in her Soho office with a gap in her schedule, so I walked there briskly, sifting my thoughts as I marched. Jane could now potentially be kingmaker. It was time to be particularly charming.

I hadn't been there for some time and was struck that reception was a shrine to PrimaParent. The large digital screens displayed our home page and there was enough 'Last Martian' merchandise to fill a teenage fan's bedroom. Evidence of their other investments was scant. We were clearly their greatest success story and I was confident therefore that I must be something of a hero to her.

Jane greeted me with an airy kiss on each cheek. She looked surprised and we sat down in a meeting room with very little attempt from either of us at small talk.

"To what do I owe the pleasure of your visit? We don't see you here that often." After four years of working with her on our board, there wasn't much of a friendship. I actually knew very little about her. She wore a wedding ring and often talked about her son, but he could have been a toddler or graduating university and her husband a vicar or a fireman for all I knew. It was too late to find out.

"I need to talk to you about a sensitive subject, I'm afraid."

"Has your rash come back?" she replied unexpectedly. I had no recollection of her having a sense of humour.

"No, all good, the cream has worked a treat. It's Julian. There's going to be some unpleasantness."

That was a bit of an understatement, but Jane did not seem surprised.

"It's been clear to us all for some time that you've become the Charles and Diana of the digital world."

"Who's who?"

"What does it matter? But something needs to be done. Why are you here today?"

I am, as you will have realised, too honest about my emotions for my own good. Entrepreneurial success is surely not defined by a need to confess. Well, not for most normal leaders. If you ask me an innocuous question, I'll answer with excessive detail, and when given this chance to describe recent events, I got disproportionately passionate in describing my outrage. Looking back at that meeting,

I may have acted like he'd run off with my wife and burnt my house down. I talked breathlessly, waving my hands like a manic orchestra conductor. After several minutes, I remembered I was not alone and perhaps it would be wise to let Jane join in the conversation.

"Sorry, I got a bit carried away. You can see what this means to me. Just as long as I've done enough to ensure that Julian gets a bullet in the head."

"What a nice analogy."

"We could use poison if you feel more comfortable."

Jane was impassive, and I knew that the more I pushed her, the more likely it would make her do the opposite. She was smiling, which I took to be a good sign. "Alex, I can't give you an answer now, you know that."

"Of course. I just wanted to furnish you with the facts objectively, to help you make the correct fiduciary decision."

"Extremely magnanimous of you." She was proving more adept at sarcasm than me. "Rest assured that when you do call a board meeting, we will protect the interests of the shareholders, don't you worry."

She clearly did not want further discussion and got up to go to another meeting. Her last words, tossed aimlessly over her shoulder as she left, encouraged me that the vote was mine. "I really appreciate you coming today. We will always put the business above the needs of any one individual. We really are very good judges of character."

She smiled, although I wasn't sure if she actually winked at me or simply had a squint. Either way, I returned to the office convinced that my morning of canvassing had resulted in a controlling share of the business backing me.

I now needed to prepare for the meeting and draft my victory speech.

* * *

I phoned Nigel later that day. Any bad PR might be detrimental to his reputation and his mercurial and provocative personality could create havoc at such a sensitive time. Nevertheless, we had developed a strong relationship. Sarah and I also socialised often with him and Kate, to whom he had been married for over a year. She was six months pregnant; Nigel had softened in anticipation of fatherhood and his cavalier swagger was less overt. I was fairly comfortable that this call would not take too long.

He insisted on making it a FaceTime call as he was staying at his Mallorcan villa and wanted me to feel jealous of the enormous sea-facing balcony in the newly built palace. The sky and sea were so bright blue, I needed sunglasses. In London, the constant drizzle painted everything slate grey.

"One day, you know, I may even invite you here, Alex, although we will probably have to wait for a cancellation from one of our celebrity friends."

"Fantastic. A holiday with you. What's the second prize? Anyway, Nigel, lovely as it is to be abused by you some more, I have something I need to share."

"Well, make it pithy. I am actually trying to write at the moment. It is in your interests that I am not disturbed." There was a vintage Remington typewriter, a coffee cup and an overflowing ashtray on the table beside him. It was as if he had art-directed the call to accentuate his old-school approach to the writer's craft.

I explained the situation quickly. Julian wanted me out. I wanted Julian out and would prevail in the ensuing boardroom battle. There was an external risk of Clyde Pilestone's empire being caught in the crossfire, which he needed to know. Nigel was a little surprised and stared silently out to sea. Something about his surroundings gave him the power, especially as I was positioned uncomfortably in the corner of an anonymous coffee shop, trying not to shout too loudly over the collective din of other people's conversations. The reply, when it eventually came, was not quite what I had expected.

"I am pretty disappointed by this and need to chat it through with Kate. We thought you were a good team together. Julian's ballsy negotiating offsets your scatter-gun enthusiasm. What worries me is that you may not be such a strong organisation after the divorce."

"You should have more faith. The team is loyal to me and there's a depth of talent now that means we are not only reliant on us. We have lawyers, agents and finance bods coming out of every filing cabinet. Anything Julian can do, they can do better."

"Well, that's your version. We'll have to see. Alex, you are my friend. You know how much I like you. Beneath all the banter, I even have a soupçon of respect for you. But I have entrusted you with my genius and I only did this because I believed in your start-up. If it unravels, we may have to think differently. Keep me informed and if you are going to execute your partner, do it cleanly."

The last sentence seemed straight out of a Sicilian self-help book and left me little other option but to assure him that my ruthlessness was well honed. It seems that severing a partnership unpleasantly is akin to assassination, given the recurrence of the analogy in all my discussions. Nigel that day inadvertently reminded me that our friendship and business relationship were separate, and the latter could be ended without affecting the former. I was going to need to show what I had always suspected: to be successful, you had to be uncompromising.

* * *

The next day, my mother phoned. We hadn't spoken for several weeks. I immediately felt guilty and vulnerable.

"Why are you calling, Mum? Is everyone all right? I have a frantic day today, so I can't really chat."

"Have you spoken to your sister?"

"No, why, is she OK?"

"Alex, please stop sounding so defensive. We have not reached the stage that we can only speak at some point of disaster."

"All right, point taken. So, what about Judith?"

"She has some amazing news. I'm not sure why she hasn't phoned. It's confidential, which I know is an alien concept to you, but I want you to hear it immediately."

Judith was at that moment in a refugee camp on the Turkish border. She spent so much time out of the country, it was hard to find time to talk. My mother's voice cracked with emotion.

"She's just been awarded an OBE for Services to Charity. It won't be public until the next Honours list is published. How wonderful for her. Isn't she special?"

Bloody irritating, more like. My baby sister had shown me up again, and although I was too old to thump her, I had every intention of pulling her braid next time I saw her. I couldn't have been happier.

"That's amazing, Mum. I'm unbelievably proud of her. She's going to have to curtsy before The Queen. And she calls herself a republican!" Succumbing to sentimentality, my eyes moistened. Judith had been rightly recognised for her boundless commitment to improve the world.

"She's really done something special with her life, hasn't she?" my mother asked with undisguised edge. A better son would have accepted this unconditional love for a child as free from implied criticism of the older, more commercially focused sibling. Sadly, my emotional balance was already askew in anticipation of imminent war with Julian.

"Why would you put it like that, Mum?'

"Like what?"

"Always comparing us."

"Are you such a narcissist, Alex, that you think I'm telling you about Judith to belittle your achievements? Believe it or not, this call is about her, not you."

Retreating, and like a naughty child caught with a hand in the biscuit tin, I sheepishly replied: "Well, I wouldn't put it past you. I know I'm not that popular with you both at the moment."

"And this is another reason why I'm calling. I wanted to tell you in person because you need to realise this is a wonderful chance to move on from your argument with your father. If we celebrate something special, maybe you'll remember the value of the family that loves you."

I knew she was right. Judith's unconditional goodness deserved to be celebrated. My father could get over his antipathy to PrimaParent and I would consider forgiving him his callousness in attacking me so publicly. Mum was wise and I was foolish. This was the opportunity to back myself out of the corner into which my anger had driven me.

Unfortunately, at that moment I saw the lift doors open and Julian and Dimitri emerge into the vast open-plan office. They were laughing in complicity, suggesting they couldn't be more relaxed with each other, or that they had just announced their engagement. I had never seen this before and would have characterised their previous interactions as frosty to the point of indifference. Julian looked over at me and smiled smugly. He started to walk to where I was sitting. My family news was, at that point, an unwelcome intrusion.

"So sorry, Mum, I can't deal with this now. I have to go. I'll think about what you said."

I ended the call abruptly, all the time not averting my gaze from the rapidly approaching Julian. He stopped in front of me and contemptuously looked me up and down. I wasn't sure if he was going to slap my face and challenge me to a duel.

"Alex."

"Julian."

"I just want you to know I've called an Extraordinary Board Meeting for 9 a.m. tomorrow, which George is convening. You need to be there. It promises to be entertaining."

With that, he spun on his heels like a well-drilled soldier and skipped back to the lifts without a care in the world.

22. Execution

I left the office almost immediately and met my lawyer at Moshe's hotel suite. Julian had stolen the initiative by calling the meeting and producing an agenda with one item on it – 'CEO Vote of Confidence'. The board had been convened with a brief email from George suggesting the 'urgent resolution of a seemingly intractable management conflict'.

Rather than it being a coup in which I controlled the army, it was now a general election with only some vague opinion polls to guide us as to its outcome. I had to rely on my belief that my integrity would triumph over Julian's superficial opportunism. The lawyers would only tell me the implications of success or defeat on our future share ownership. If I lost, I'd keep my shares but have no influence whatsoever on the day-to-day direction of the business.

Inevitably, I didn't sleep much that night. My mind twisted and pivoted as I tried to scenario-plan, but in the end I simply catastrophised. What if something went wrong? Had Dimitri turned against me? How biased would George be towards Julian? Would I be able to outstare my unflappable nemesis? I listened to the interminable silence of the night and grew progressively sadder that, despite a flourishing business, my life was underpinned by unpleasantness and dispute. Eventually I fell asleep at about 5.30 a.m. and was totally disoriented by my shrill alarm a few minutes later.

Standing under the shower for an age trying to wake up, I rehearsed the script we'd drafted the day before. I dressed in a navy suit and open-necked white shirt and stared in the mirror, contemplating whether I looked like a leader or a follower. Sarah came up behind me and encircled my waist with a supportive hug.

"Remember, Alex, you're a killer," she said unconvincingly.

"Am I, though? I always saw myself more as a romantic poet."

"Your verse is not going to help you now. You may need to toughen up a bit, at least for the morning."

"You realise, in the event I lose, I'm out?"

"If you agree to do the school run occasionally and sort out your comic collection, it's a small price to pay."

"I'd better win then."

* * *

At 9 a.m. the meeting room filled with the board members, although I had arrived a few minutes early to compose myself. There was a strained and awkward silence as everyone poured themselves a coffee. Julian did not make eye contact but had a self-satisfied smirk that I found unsettling.

Dimitri, Alice and Samantha had been invited as shareholders. Alice tried to give me encouraging nods as she took her place, but Dimitri stared at me like I was a stranger sitting opposite him on the Tube. Brooke and Cole were next to one another, looking like the happiest couple in the world, their marital status decidedly confusing. Moshe, inevitably finishing a phone call, was talking angrily in Hebrew, his head shaking in frustration and his faced fixed in a scowl. The meeting was brought to order with a short introduction from George on the reason it was taking place. It sounded like a list of my faults and inadequacies.

"I am afraid we have to resolve a delicate situation in order to protect all of us as shareholders. It has become increasingly apparent that the working relationship between the co-founders and CEOs has become untenable. Julian has discussed, with me and others, his belief that the business would be better served by the removal of Alex as co-CEO and I have convened this meeting to make an immediate decision in the interests of the business and its ongoing success. It gives me no pleasure as chairman to have to ensure that a resolution is achieved."

Actually, it felt like he was getting quite a lot of pleasure from my discomfort, and when he finished he looked towards Julian with paternal concern. My attempts to canvass support had been superseded by the reality that I was now on trial. This was further illustrated by Julian, laying out his case with the fervour of a prosecutor prowling in front of a jury. I was surprised he didn't put on a wig and gown.

I won't replay his speech, which became a bit of a blur as I half-listened, simultaneously preparing my rebuttal. It was hard to hear and subsequently painful to recall, as his argument was disarmingly plausible. He told everyone I was a very decent hard-working person of good intent. He emphasised that the business had been built and driven by my vision and I was brimming with good ideas and positive energy. My chutzpah (which he always pronounced incorrectly as *shoootzpar*) had managed to secure the Clyde Pilestone deal, which had catapulted us to global success.

The problem, he argued, was that I was not a good leader. He was certain I was not cut out for the scale and complexity of a multi-country business, and nor did I have the ruthlessness to do what was necessary for its success. He reminded them that when we had our first global get-together, I was laughed on to stage, and not in a good way. He made countless allegations that senior team members were always complaining to him that I did not make decisions quickly enough. He mentioned a couple of recent unsuccessful senior hires that I had overseen. I was evidently too soft a judge of character.

Julian read out an email from Clark Templeton, our jargon-infested Harvard *wunderkind* in charge of new product development. Given the contempt Julian had shown him, I was amazed to hear that he was extremely concerned by my 'profit-negative indecisiveness' and 'suboptimal excessive emotional engagement' in reaching business decisions. There were several similar statements from senior individuals, all implying that our growing pains were the result of my weakness as a leader. He then progressed to the inexorable demise of our working marriage, resulting in a fractured and untenable relationship. He contended I was jealous of his commercial flair. As a consequence, I was secretive, obstructive and sarcastic to the point that conversations with me descended into a relentless attempt to prove my wittiness.

His *coup de grâce* in this *coup d'état* was an email from Nigel, in which he made it clear to Julian that my dismissal would not affect our publishing money machine. He stated that despite his personal relationship with me, his commercial partnership was with the business and as long as his interests were being protected, we could bring in 'Donald Duck or Donald Trump to run the business for all I care'. Naively, I expected the fond recollection of copying my chemistry homework aged fourteen would prevail and he would view my presence as non-negotiable. Clearly not.

Julian spoke for what seemed an eternity, but, with a quick glance at the clock, I realised was only ten minutes. When he sat down, he looked at me directly and held up his hand to stop any interruption. He tilted his head as if he was a carer talking to a poorly patient.

"Alex. You have to understand that this is not a reflection of what I feel for you. I know you are so ambitious for this business to be successful. You won't believe me now, but this is the best way for you to achieve this."

I was quite proud of my reaction – an obdurate silence. I did not want to engage in a conversation, so I stared back at him, feeling the collective awkwardness deepen across the room. I then began my direct and abrasive defence, focusing on Julian's untrustworthiness. Starting with the loan for his legal bill and then his rock-and-roll lifestyle expenses, I suggested that his attitude to the business was one of entitlement. Despite a global footprint, he saw it as his private fiefdom. He dipped in and out of his responsibilities as it pleased him and loved the thrill of commercial negotiation, running away from oversight of ongoing operations or the nurturing of our people. He was keener on a good personal profile in a glossy magazine than a positive corporate story in the business pages.

I stressed that, contrary to Julian's version, the management team looked to me for guidance and support. I knew that their loyalty was unwavering, citing recent conversations about their concern that Julian was obstructive to the daily operational needs of the business. Looking at Alice, Dimitri and Samantha, I restated their trust in me and their frequent misgivings about Julian's unpleasant or indifferent behaviour. Dimitri stared fixedly at his shoes every time I mentioned his name. My final words were delivered with a pre-rehearsed flourish of sincerity to emphasise that my leadership was the only sensible way forward.

"Julian has suggested I am not strong enough to match my hopes for the business with the mental toughness to make difficult decisions. It's easy to make a glib comment like that if you are more interested in the trappings of success than the rigour and hard work needed to sustain its growth. I want to run this company properly. I need to be allowed to do so without fighting my partner. This is not a popularity contest. It is a vote of competence."

'Vote of competence'. I thought that was particularly clever when I dreamt it up a few days previously. Instead of spontaneous applause and perhaps some gentle singing from a celestial choir, there was only silence, punctured by the sound of Julian's laughter. He clapped his hands together and said, "Hard luck, old boy. You'll find that I've repaid the loan, and Samantha and I have just gone through all my expenses. Anything you might have deemed questionable, I've settled up. You'll struggle to dismiss me for owing money and having unreasonable expense claims."

I glanced at Samantha as if to say *what the hell?* and she shrugged her shoulders helplessly.

George outlined what would happen next. Julian and I had to leave the room and the board would discussion a solution. Since the motion was my dismissal, he was going to canvass the opinion of the room and ascertain who had the most equity favouring them. It was that brutal. As we left, there was an awkward moment when we realised that to return to our respective desks, we had to walk in the same direction. Since striding in silence down a long corridor would make a bad day worse, I gestured for him to go first and waited a few minutes before following.

I flopped into a chair in a quiet corner of the vast open-plan space and saw a text from my mother, which simply read: *Call me now to discuss trip to the Palace.* I had judiciously avoided any contact since the phone call about Judith's gong, and knew I couldn't run away from my family for that much longer. However, I had done enough arguing that day and instead called Sarah to tell her about the morning's activity. As it clicked through to voicemail, I realised that she was in a clinic. Like a child on the first day in a new big school, I suddenly felt apprehensive and alone. The meeting had been disarmingly short. It was feasible that I hadn't won. In the far corner, I could see Julian with his feet on the desk, talking animatedly into his phone.

After forty minutes, we were called back and had to enter the room awkwardly without speaking to one another. I contemplated tripping him up as he walked through the door ahead of me, but reason prevailed. No one looked at me. If that felt bad, the presence of our corporate lawyer made me even more uncomfortable. George did not equivocate in delivering a judgement.

"Alex. I am afraid you have lost this battle. You do not have enough support from the shareholders. We had a vote, based on our respective holdings. Brooke, Moshe, Alice and Samantha supported you. Cole, Jane, Dimitri and the others were for Julian, who also had my support. I am sure you can do the arithmetic. You were well short of a working majority. Therefore, we believe it is untenable for you to carry on in your role as CEO and we would ask for your resignation. You can have the conversation now with the lawyers or, as I suggest, you let the news sink in at home for a day or so, and then we sort out the detail. Either way, I am afraid that on behalf of us all, we have to thank you for your energy and enthusiasm in creating this wonderful business, and promise that you can rest assured of its continued successful stewardship after your departure."

He raised his hand towards me. I quickly realised that rather than a consoling handshake, he was gesticulating towards the door through which he expected me to leave immediately. Dazed, I hobbled lamely to the door, which Cole had leapt up enthusiastically to open. I didn't really look round but, as I left, I caught momentary sight of a tearful Alice mouthing "I'm sorry." Somehow, my scrambled brain told me to maintain dignity in my departure. Quite hard, when all you feel is pain.

* * *

I don't want to dwell too much on the state of my mind for the next few days. Leaving the meeting was humiliating. I tried some deep yoga breaths to calm me down as I walked out, but I didn't know what I was doing other than hyperventilating. Sitting in a taxi having lost control of my company, my heart was racing, tears welled in my eyes and I was overcome with one rising and uncontrollable emotion. Fury.

How dare they do this to me. This was not about my ability, but rather Julian's need to win. Leadership is often jettisoned from an organisation for reasons of incompetence and poor performance. At that moment, some four years after we launched, we were valued at over £450m. We had five hundred staff in fifteen countries. We may not have been a fully grown unicorn, but we were certainly a mythical creature of some sort.

You may have found this narrative mawkish and think I am too emotional to succeed at this level. Maybe, despite my bias, Julian's minor-celebrity glitz makes you inclined to sympathise with him. I don't really care, because when I was ejected from my own business, I had the seething indignation of an Old Testament God disappointed in the way his creation had turned out. Vain Julian, psychotic Dimitri and pompous George were all in my sights.

The accusation that had been levelled at me many times was that I was a nice enough bloke, but a bit soft. I definitely had a set of values I tried to follow: be polite, be kind, remember the feelings of others. They can sustain and fuel ambition but sometimes get in the way, and I convinced myself that, until I signed any paperwork, this was not over. You can't overturn the results of a general election but perhaps you can order a recount if you feel that the maths wasn't correct.

Sarah tried to talk to me, but I didn't really engage. I told her that I needed to be alone and figure out a solution. I could tell that she wanted me to accept defeat graciously and return to some form of family normalcy. She argued that I had created a company that had made us wealthy beyond reasonable expectation. Indeed, if I sold out, we'd be incredibly wealthy. Imagine what a happy life we could have, not to mention the good we could do. She repeated this whenever she could.

In total exasperation late one evening, when I was totally unresponsive to her argument, she lost her cool and shouted, "Alex. I have been a total bloody saint over the last five years. I have stood by as you have left the family to seek your fortune. You have not been there for us, so I am begging you to give up. You have lost, Julian has won, and yes, he is a complete shit. He betrayed his wife and now he has betrayed you. Maybe he'll get his comeuppance. Catherine has moved on and now you need to."

Her passion inspired a totally different reaction to what she had hoped for. I felt a surge of excitement and gave her a huge and unexpected hug. It was not because she had outlined a happy future. It was because she had used the words 'comeuppance' and 'Catherine' in such close proximity. Suddenly my path to redemption was clear, as I recalled the conversation Julian and I had had about his divorce.

Julian had won the majority of support based, perhaps, on a false assumption of share ownership. I ran out of the kitchen, leaving a bemused Sarah wondering why I was so skittish. Shutting the door to my study, I phoned Catherine.

* * *

We met for breakfast the next day. Catherine was suspicious of why I needed to see her urgently and it had taken some cajoling to alter her schedule, but I made it clear that it was crucial to her financial well-being. As soon as we ordered coffee, I told her what had happened.

"Well, Catherine, I know how it feels to be dumped by Julian too."

Not the most sensitive opening remark, I realised. It was met with angry admonishment.

"What on earth are you talking about?"

"Julian has led an uprising and I've been fired so that he can be sole CEO. I'm out."

Her face maintained its sternness. She didn't seem that surprised. "I'm sorry to hear this, but these things happen, and often do when Julian wants his way. You must be devastated, Alex. But what has it got to do with me? I'm not a member of the board."

"No, but you have an interest in his shares, don't you?"

She didn't respond and was not making this easy.

"Julian told me he was arguing with you over the value of the company as part of your settlement."

"I'm amazed he did that. He knows our negotiations are confidential and, with enormous respect, Alex, you have a mouth the size of Cheddar Gorge. I really wouldn't want you to know my interests. What you probably think is that I'm stealing your precious company when all I'm trying to do is protect my children."

She couldn't have been more wrong. Well, except the bit about my big mouth.

"That's not fair. Sarah and I always felt that you had been treated terribly by Julian. Really, we did. Which brings me to a crucial question. I don't need to know all the details, but please answer this. Do you have control of more than 30 per cent of Julian's equity?"

She paused for a second, as if contemplating a marriage vow, and then slowly nodded, looking me directly in the eye. "I do."

"Then, if you're interested, we can both enjoy a spot of rather pleasant revenge."

* * *

I don't know how I expected her to react. In the event, it certainly wasn't glee, rather a muted sadness. She listened to my war story and the legal advice I had been given. If we could prove that Julian did not have full control of his equity because it was part of his divorce settlement, then he did not have the necessary support of the board. I had won.

Catherine eventually pledged her full commitment to me. It was not because she particularly sympathised with my plight. I'm not even sure she really liked or respected me that much. Rather, she was angered and saddened by Julian's enduring dishonesty. She didn't want her children to grow up benefiting from the spoils of his lack of decency. If he felt impelled always to do what suited him, she, conversely, was going to do what was right for everyone else.

Five days after the first meeting, I convened another emergency gathering of the board. I was reliant on the tenacity and aggression of my lawyers to ensure the legality of my actions and they, in turn, faced a barrage of angry responses from George and Julian. But to no avail, and despite Brooke and Cole being back in the US and only on video, we gathered late one Tuesday afternoon in the same meeting room. I had managed to invoke a procedural misdemeanour as the reason for a second vote, allowing me to keep my new ally a secret from the enemy.

Of course, I had confided in Moshe a few days earlier what was going to happen. He was malevolently elated when I revealed my strategy on the phone to him, shrieking the same bizarre phrase: 'You are a business commando after all.' He told me that I needed to exert maximum pain on Julian, which was ironic given that he had seemed tacitly to support him in the first boardroom battle. Still, the ensuing narrative appealed to my sense of the theatrical – after all, I had nothing to lose other than my dignity.

I had been able to keep my secret well. Julian and George maintained a glacial silence when I entered the room with my lawyer, doing everything they could through hostile body language to maximise my discomfort. I must have irritated them significantly because I could not stop smirking and had to stop myself from singing aloud, *I know something you don't, na na na na na*. George refused to look up from his papers and muttered with ill-concealed contempt, "Can we begin this farcical waste of time."

I was by now feeling immortal, so decided to challenge his rudeness. "Well, that's not a very chairman-like way to begin a meeting, George."

He looked up sharply, his face suggesting he was contemplating having me bumped off. I grabbed my phone and, like a teenager ignoring a parent, pressed send on a text to Alice, giving her the signal to make an entrance. Then, in a benign and soothing voice, I simply said: "Please can we wait thirty seconds. I have asked someone to join the meeting."

I counted the seconds in my head, staring at a ceiling tile, afraid to catch Julian's eye for fear of giggling, bursting into tears or turning into a pillar of salt. Eventually, the heavy door opened, and a timid and apprehensive Catherine entered with Alice. I made the introductions with a triumphant flourish, suggesting I had finally become nasty in pursuit of my dream.

"Julian, I believe you know your ex-wife."

His face crumpled into a look of horror, like someone accidently stepping into an empty lift shaft and hurtling to an unpleasant demise. He knew what I was doing and that he had been outflanked. The other protagonists could not disguise their emotions. Moshe was loving every minute, Alice and Samantha were struggling to contain their excitement. Jane was relatively indifferent, making me realise that she didn't care about people, only a healthy return. I was thrilled to see the discomfort of the perfidious Dimitri. He tried to be very friendly, anticipating the success of my putsch. His charm was unconvincing and my response to it decidedly lukewarm. Catherine looked extremely sad – torn between a desire for justice, residual love for Julian and resentment at my palpable smugness at victory. After all, my gain was her loss of a marriage.

George was petulantly argumentative, questioning the process aggressively. Fortunately, his arrogance was met with the meticulous calm of my legal team. We made it clear that Catherine had ownership and hence voting rights, therefore the first decision was invalid. I almost skipped out of the room when we were asked to leave once more for the voting, and made the immature gesture of elaborately holding the door open for Julian, who shuffled down the corridor with drooping shoulders.

His dismissal twenty minutes later was brief. Moshe delivered the news to him, because in our absence he had successfully wrenched the role of chairman from a seething George. Moshe's summary was bereft of sympathy.

"I find it hard to thank you, Julian, for your efforts as I dismiss you. I really have never trusted you and so I am not that sorry to see you go. Alex has our full support now. He has shown that he is tougher than we have all given him credit for. It's a new era and, Julian, you are going to miss all the good bits."

Calmly, Julian rose from his chair and spoke briefly to Catherine, touching her lightly and affectionately on the shoulder. He gathered his things and walked towards me with a broad grin. Unruffled as ever, he shook my hand and smiled enigmatically.

"Well played, Alex. You have won and surprised us all. I'm still a major shareholder and will be watching with much interest how you get on. Interesting times ahead. Interesting times."

With that, the ship was mine.

23. Dawn Chorus

There was little time for celebration or recrimination. No sooner had we signed the paperwork for Julian's departure than we were raided by the Information Commissioner's Office, the flying squad of data protection.

A dawn raid was a bit old hat for us. Except this time, it wasn't the police weeding out opportunistic drug dealers, but a serious operational challenge based on alleged shady practices. The Information Commissioner might sound like an upmarket librarian but is actually a senior government official able to levy a whopping fine, instigate criminal proceedings, accelerate a parliamentary sub-committee investigation or just create reputational mayhem. After an initial consultation with our lawyers, it seemed we might be in for all four.

For an ethical business rooted in family life, it appeared we had not behaved well. There was evidently a political opportunity to castigate our arrogant ambition and reveal the shoddy practices prevalent in pushy digital businesses. They came at us all spreadsheets blazing with the initial raid, accompanied by the theatricality of a press tip-off ensuring obtrusive cameras and aggressive journalists. It wasn't quite the scrum you'd get at the announcement of a royal baby, but it was unpleasant to have to push my way through the melee while avoiding my natural instinct to proclaim innocence to anyone that would listen.

At the heart of the case was the worrying revelation that we had used the database of a supermarket's loyalty scheme to hack our early growth. With chilling certainty, I remembered when Dimitri told us that he had got hold of some data from some faceless online associate on the dark web, as a return for a favour. He made it clear to us it was completely safe, and we should just get on with it without being so conservative.

It was a time of mounting political interference through nefarious data manipulation. How else could one account for Trump or Brexit? A commercial enterprise stealing the shopping-basket information of innocent people across the country was, therefore, a breach too far. A great story, particularly in a quieter news week.

We were a large enough organisation to throw money at professional help, hiring a top crisis management PR agency and some eye-wateringly expensive data protection lawyers. At a furious Moshe's behest, a team of 'data security' experts arrived to make our previous behaviour opaque where possible, sort of like clearing a dodgy internet history.

A meeting room was commandeered, blinds drawn, coffee machines, printers and paper shredders logged into a separate hacker-proof network. At no stage did anyone ask us the obvious question, 'Did you do it?' We were a death-row murderer establishing a robust defence without ever being asked if we'd pulled the trigger. Actually, it was all rather exciting. Having recently risen from the dead like the better-known biblical Lazarus, I was feeling invincible. This was just another test I needed to pass to show I was a calm statesman in a crisis.

Despite the pressure, I was revelling in the palpable discomfort of Dimitri, who could sense his imminent demise, which I hoped to accelerate. He had shown no loyalty in the battle with Julian and there was no need to protect him. What an opportunity to pin all the blame on him. I was settling my scores.

The charges were more than just stealing data. Unbeknown to me, we had allowed Moshe's team at SmickSmack to have access to our own global database. His initial financial support had been predicated on giving Avi Ram unfettered access to our back-end engine.

He hoped our growing consumer brand would help the encrypted security products he was developing for retail businesses. His reasoning was vague and, besides, we just wanted to get the company going, so we didn't really challenge him as much as we clearly should have. Moshe's corporate empire boasted a Byzantine and impenetrable structure and, with no official UK or EU office, was judicially hard to pin down. Not so his naive associates, who had left footprints and fingerprints all over the crime scene.

A fidgety Dimitri came to see me a day after the raid. We had hardly spoken since the boardroom theatrics, so I cultivated a nonchalant 'you mean nothing to me' demeanour; feet up on the desk, scrolling through emails and ignoring his desperate need for eye contact.

"How much trouble are we in, Alex?"

"We?"

"This affects us all, surely?"

"Of course it does. But you might want to consider getting some legal representation, as a lot of the accusations have your name attached to them. This could potentially be a criminal offence." I was really enjoying this now. *Good karma,* as they say in ruthless Buddhist circles.

"Alex, you know very well that we took the decision together that day. You, me and Julian. This is about all of us."

"What day are you referring to? I remember many conversations with you in the early days about hacking growth, but I don't remember sanctioning you to embark on a supermarket sweep of illegal data."

My memory was, however, entirely clear about him procuring a 'dark web favour'. He had chided me for my nervousness and, like a reluctant schoolboy encouraged to go shoplifting with his naughtier friends, I had sanctioned the crime with Julian. There was fortunately no evidence of this conversation.

Dimitri looked at me with confused horror. I had always been a constant support, unconditionally encouraging, irrespective of his mercurial behaviour. He must have realised this change of attitude stemmed from his siding with my enemy, and his brilliant mind, bereft of any natural empathy, could not cope with the withdrawal of affection. He shook his head and stuttered the plea "Please do the right thing" as he sloped back to his desk, shoulders visibly sagging. Any pleasure was momentary, my conscience reminding me that cruelty was not a sign of good leadership.

This was further confirmed when I recounted the story to Sarah. I thought she would exonerate me with the passion of a lioness protecting her young. Instead, she called me a callous bastard, and said that irrespective of the provocation, she was ashamed that I would take pleasure in revenging a perceived wrong. I went to bed rather embarrassed by my inability once more to separate personal slight from professional behaviour.

The next day, Clark Templeton came to see me, oozing false bonhomie. Since Julian's departure, he had become my de facto deputy through the insistence of Moshe and Brooke. It was hard not to have a cordial relationship with him, because he was ineffably polite and solicitous to everyone. That he was driven by a sense of his own worth, believing his voice to be the wisest, was the real threat I feared.

He had been highly efficient in conceiving new revenue streams. In the space of eighteen months, he had developed a huge new initiative for us, PrimaParent Learn. Rightly, he argued that above entertaining their children, parents wanted them to have the best education possible to prepare for their future. Since we were about providing unparalleled experiences, surely parents would be prepared to pay for additional learning support for their kids. Technology made this easy to roll out globally. If we could safely recruit retailers and experience providers, we could certainly also enlist the brightest and best tutors available. Cleverly, we were ahead of our time, teaching remotely using basic video services like Skype.

Buoyed by his unassailable importance to the business, increasingly he treated me with a benign condescension. He would pretend to defer to my CEO decisions, but his eyes would stare through me, pondering an alternative opinion like a satellite navigation system automatically rerouting on encountering traffic.

He grabbed me shortly after my conversation with Dimitri and asked if he could have a quiet chat. The war room was free from lawyers and consultants and we sat at the enormous oak meeting table with our coffee, surrounded by a rainforest of paper. Clark looked concerned, choosing his words precisely to suggest he only cared for my well-being.

"How are you holding up, Alex? It must be difficult." His head tilted sympathetically.

"No, I'm good. We'll get through this relatively unscathed, I'm sure."

"Of course we will. I just have one thought I'd like to run past you." His head was at a normal businesslike angle now, his eyes fixed at some point beyond my shoulder.

"Go on."

"I've been talking with the team and to Moshe."

"To Moshe? Why do you need to speak to him?"

"He calls me to pick my brains from time to time." Suddenly, I felt less invincible. Moshe always had an agenda in any conversation.

"And?"

"And we think you should not be the public face of the company through this crisis."

"Why would that be? It's not pleasant, but it is very much my role."

"I want to put this diplomatically."

"Thank you, Henry Kissinger."

"Everyone thinks I will be better."

* * *

Just as I had wrested back control, I felt the queasy uncertainty of a different but equally ambitious rival seeking to topple me. A covert insurrection had gathered pace, believing the urbane preppy persona of Clark better suited to intense media scrutiny than an emotional 'heart on the sleeve' sort of chap like me. My position as CEO was being undermined by a collective lack of faith in my ability to stay calm and measured under pressure.

I still led the legal response to the investigation, but my every move was accompanied by Clark at my side, nodding in vigorous agreement or sagely suggesting a better alternative. He was always respectful, just not that helpful.

For a couple of weeks, Clark was the king of interviews. Our stated position was that we hadn't known about the arrival of the data and it had most likely been brought into the company by a contractor or former employee. Clearly, we were appalled by the revelation and were instigating a full, transparent review of our procedures. The Information Commissioner wanted to push for the maximum fine available (£500,000), having also found other consent breaches in some of our activity that infringed the new GDPR law. More worryingly. the National Crime Agency was also investigating us to see if serious fraud had taken place.

In this febrile mood, Clark proved an adept ambassador for the business. He was unruffled and articulate. Even a feisty *Newsnight* grilling did not faze him and his engaging performance had a foundation of gravitas. I was consumed with resentment but still had a few unglamorous challenges of my own. First, I had to fire Dimitri. We all knew that he had pushed our initial growth independently of any compliance with data protection. He tried to argue in our internal investigation that Julian and I had been complicit. I was affronted by the accusation and denied it vehemently, even thinking of adding 'liar, liar, pants on fire' for emphasis. Fortunately, Dimitri was no longer irreplaceable now that we had grown. We could happily choose from many candidates at other digital behemoths.

His exit was undramatic – having surrendered to its inevitability, he was resigned to his fate. His former guileless persona briefly returned, and he thanked me repeatedly for the opportunity of a lifetime, declaring that he would never again experience the adrenaline-fuelled pleasure of our early days. The unexpectedly amicable parting allowed Alice and I to take him for a valedictory dinner, at which we relived some of his more unreasonable and extreme behaviour through a sentimental mist that rendered it harmless.

Negotiations concluded with a generous settlement. In return for his future silence and discretion, his shareholding remained intact and he left a very wealthy individual. I had no qualms about precipitating his departure, though I was slightly uncomfortable that blame for the investigation was not collective, but exclusively his. Self-preservation can breed some amoral behaviours.

After a month of intense scrutiny, it seemed we had weathered the initial onslaught. Clark was reputationally enhanced, with a genuine external profile. He would swagger through the office like a politician elected to high office, stopping short of developing a presidential wave. On the other hand, bruised and insecure, I needed the organisation to give me a cuddle. My mood was not enhanced by a rare text one evening from a caustic Nigel, who informed me that *that preppie minion of yours has made you look more of a moron than even posh Julian in his heyday.*

The investigation was not over at all, in fact, and although we escaped criminal action, we were due a hefty fine from the Information Commissioner. Of more concern was the political pressure now being applied. Gordon Hardcastle, Labour MP for Cleethorpes and Chairman of the Commons Cross-Party Communications Committee, was incensed by our unprincipled greed. He tabled an Early Day Motion in Parliament, which did not hold back.

This House believes the alleged data breaches by PrimaParent, currently investigated by the Information Commissioner, represent the ethical decline of digital businesses engaged in securing unicorn status and require agreed guidelines for start-up businesses with additional legal redress if the pursuit of customer acquisition comes at the expense of data protection.

MPs flocked to sign the motion and the ensuing debate about start-up culture received widespread coverage. Buoyed by parliamentary support, Gordon Hardcastle pushed for a formal review of our operational practices, to be heard in front of his sub-committee. Clark, adept at avoiding personal involvement in this growing battle, claimed it was inappropriate for an American to challenge the sovereignty of a foreign government. How convenient for him that it was me who was summoned to appear in front of the committee when the investigation became miraculously fast-tracked.

I was not helped by the very forceful investigation that also began into our principal backers. An organisation will inherit the DNA of its funders and it didn't take much to link us to the values of our well-known investors. Moshe was offensively portrayed as a mysterious Israeli tech maven, presumably a Mossad agent looking to foment political instability. Brooke and Cole's increasingly separate public lives, coupled with some bitter war stories from failed companies they had supported, made them the manifestation of Silicon Valley venality.

Lord George Dobson was now also a magnet for controversy. His high-profile support of the Conservative Party undoubtedly energised Gordon Hardcastle's quest for blood. To make matters worse, he was now implicated in a growing scandal emanating from his partnership with a Chinese company on a massive new City development. It turned out that a significant sum of money could be traced back to the Chinese government, who were looking to curry favour with our political establishment in return for telecommunication contracts.

Let me summarise these machinations. Clark was now a hero and I was a paranoid chump. Because of my undeclared complicity, we were going to be fined significantly. Verbose and overemotional, I had been summoned for a grilling in Parliament. The world thought Moshe a spy and George the funder of a Chinese spy ring. Brooke and Cole's sham marriage papered the cracks of their dubious investments.

And if that wasn't enough, I was going to have to make peace with my father.

24. Home Truths

It had been nearly two years since I'd last spoken to my father. Time passed quickly as my grief at the dispute was masked by a prodigious work ethic. I had also decided that if I couldn't be a good son, I would become a better father to my own children by making an increased effort to create a set of boundaries around family life, which I tried to preserve. It was not necessarily about being present all of the time, so much as being less distracted by my phone. Sarah appreciated the attempt to change, joking that one day she might even leave me alone with them.

I had grown up in a close family, which, despite the contrasting temperaments and outlooks, had an unshakeable stability. The fissure of upset from our dispute was a trauma that no one expected.

My mother and I spoke regularly. When we met for coffee, we managed a short amount of idle conversation about business and domestic minutiae before she would attempt, with all her years of therapist experience, to address the underlying cause of our collective unhappiness. I did not want to peel away the layers of my anger and would close down conversation abruptly. She would try another approach, only to be met with unyielding silence.

Sarah carried on taking the children round to see them and they were devoted grandparents, carrying on as best they could in abnormal circumstances. I felt a deep sense of shame, but it did not outweigh the anger. My father had never hidden his lack of respect for my commercial drive. The more I wanted to achieve, the further I undermined the validity of his personal philosophy. Having a sister whose ambition was rooted in a desire for social change was not very helpful for me.

I would lie awake at night and reflect on my stubbornness. It seemed so unfair that I should have to be the first to back down. But as time dragged on and the argument remained unresolved, I began to realise that nothing good can come from perpetual anger. Just ask Darth Vader.

After so much recent trauma in the business, I was beginning to soften, and knew that a resolution could not be avoided. This was accelerated by a call from my sister to invite me to the Palace to see her meet The Queen and receive her OBE. She had also been trying some shuttle diplomacy between me and my father to thaw the Cold War.

"I am allowed to take three people," she told me, "and as much as I prefer Sarah, I suppose you should have first call."

"I would understand. She's a huge royalist and a much nicer human being."

"That's not in doubt, but I've known you all my life. You're like a brother to me."

"Well, I'm honoured, baby sis. I'll even iron a shirt."

"Alex, you're going to have to deal with Dad before you come. I'm not going to make Mum sit between you two in brooding silence. This has to stop. He was wrong and you have to swallow your pride. Do you think you can do that for me?"

I didn't answer because I knew she was right. It just felt like a trip to the dentist for a filling, knowing the surgery had run out of anaesthetic and the drill was a bit rusty. In the end, I told Judith how proud I was of her and that I would not ruin her day.

Fortunately, I didn't have to make the first move as the next day I received a an unexpected email from my father, saying: *Please read the attached and then call.* There was an accompanying ten-page letter – not an apology, but an attempt to effect resolution through academic discourse. It began with a calm assessment of our divorce.

This schism between us has at its root differing perspectives of the value of ambition in the construction of stable society. You are focused on its expression through wealth creation and I feel there is a validity in the aspiration for personal contentment. Perhaps we both seek a unicorn – yours monetary and mine predicated on humanist values. You would expect little less from me but rigorous evidence-based analysis. So, let me elaborate.

What followed was an examination of how the human spirit copes with its restless nature and the implications that can have for personal contentment. The conclusion (if there was one) would suggest that ambition is more likely to grow faster in better-educated, more affluent cohorts. But rooted in impatience, it is less likely to confer long-term domestic happiness or stability. Emotional well-being is more closely linked to the stability and support of a close-knit community with shared values.

The content did not matter as much as the sentiment. It was a love letter of sorts and a half-apology, derived from his belief that maximising our potential for thinking is more important than anything. He finished by saying:

My conclusion, Alex, is uncertain. I cannot tell you how to live your life. I shouldn't publicise my concerns and you need to let your anger dissolve. But I love you. You are my son and we must move on.

I called him immediately.

* * *

Several weeks later we were in the ballroom of Buckingham Palace, sitting together. It wasn't as grand as I had expected, and I whispered to my father that perhaps they needed to upgrade the carpet and curtains sometime soon. He nodded and, ever the republican, observed that tapping posh people on the shoulder with a sword should not be considered a proper job.

We had made peace to a certain extent. After I received the letter, we met that evening and had an emotional mutual tear-fest in which we both apologised, not really to each other, but mainly to our absent wives for their fortitude during our estrangement. It was implicit in our reunion that we were going to move on, but it was equally clear that neither of us wanted to probe too deeply into what had happened for fear of reigniting the conflict.

Family life returned, slightly tarnished, but sufficiently robust to withstand any more knocks. The children took it for granted that we could now all be together, and there was much excitement for the arrival of a new baby. My father and I resumed a slightly strained relationship in which we spoke politely about each other's work to avoid causing offence. It was not perfect, but my mother was relieved that we were together again, and sanguine about the cordial father-son relationship that had emerged.

When Judith received her OBE, we were all united in our pride for her achievement. The Lord Chamberlain announced her award 'for Services to Charity' and she strode shyly towards The Queen. Her curtsy secured a perfect ten from the Russian judge and I saw my mother squeeze my father's hand in mutual admiration for the wonderful person they had created.

Judith and The Queen had a good old chinwag for what seemed much longer than everyone else. At one stage, she turned her head towards us, almost introducing us to The Queen. Whatever she said, it produced much hilarity and for a moment it seemed that our monarch, free from the repetitive monotony of the ceremony, was actually enjoying herself.

When we met up with her afterwards, we all hugged and stared at her medal. The only medal I ever got was for 'most improved player' at the end of one football season when I was eleven. I teased her for being part of the Establishment.

"How are things going in the Empire these days? Are you upset we lost India?" My mother looked at me disapprovingly.

"Please ignore your jealous brother and tell us what you chatted to The Queen about. You were definitely her favourite this morning. It looked like you were having a grand old time."

"She was lovely. She asked me how my family felt about all the time I had spent in a war zone. That's when I looked in your direction."

"Why?" my father chipped in.

"I told her that it distracted my father and brother from continually arguing with each other as to who was the cleverest."

"And is that why she laughed?" I said.

"Well, it was actually when I asked if she ever had the same trouble with her family!"

* * *

A month later, my parents came to support their other child in public. This time, it was to sit in the visitors' gallery as I appeared in front of the Cross-Party Communications Committee.

Curiously, I was less nervous about the outcome than the public scrutiny and the risk of enduring YouTube notoriety because of something stupid I said. I did not want my parents to come, but Sarah was insistent on being there and my parents did not want to leave her, heavily pregnant and distressed, watching the man she loved cry like a baby on national TV. I was hoping to preserve a proud, Mount-Rushmore-like composure, but no one believed me.

That we were heading towards a massive fine was inevitable, but we were now a global operation, and it would be a blip in our healthy cash flow. While we had ever so slightly accidently broken the law, there was a media and political glee that underpinned the attempt to unravel our success. Our ascent had come too easily, so our hubris deserved a bit of unpleasantness.

The real challenge, as I awaited my grilling, was the growing realisation that I was now the focal point for our company's failings, and this made my presence at its helm much more precarious. Moshe was all over the business now. He phoned me constantly with a barrage of random questions about any aspect of our performance, personnel issues, future plans or financial performance. His continual WhatsApp messages to me were like a form of Chinese water torture. Incessant random thoughts unconnected by a single thread of conversation. *Have you done this? Have you thought about that? Why? Who? What? Where? When?* His interrogation techniques had a military precision in their clear objective to unsettle me.

He was assisted in a more insidious fashion by Brooke, who acted as my all-in-one unsolicited mentor, therapist and rabbi. She rang me constantly to ask if I was OK. She sent me eclectic articles and links, which tackled subjects including veganism in the workplace, management meditation techniques and what the Talmud can teach today's CEO.

I couldn't fathom why there was always such close proximity between the arrival of her messages and the sharper and more accusatory questioning from Moshe. It was as if they had a co-ordinated messaging strategy to maximise my disquiet. To confuse me further, it seemed that Brooke and Cole had reconciled once more and had embarked on some very public appearances to show they were still current in Silicon Valley. As for Brooke and Moshe, I had given up wondering what their relationship was, other than continually unsettling for me.

Finally, there was my overenthusiastic deputy, Clark, hovering in the background with helpful suggestions and insights. He had managed to make my parliamentary appearance sound like a good personal opportunity to raise my profile and show the world who I was. He was continually slapping me on the back and uttering war cries like 'attaboy' and 'go get 'em tiger', like I was his son about to step up to the plate to bat in a Little League baseball match.

Only the ever-loyal and empathetic Alice knew what to say. She came to find me the night before the hearing to wish me luck, bringing me a present of some extra-strong breath mints, which she presented with a flourish.

"With all that coffee you drink, there's no point offending everyone further with your halitosis."

"Very thoughtful, Alice." She was right, I could kill a man at ten paces after a double macchiato.

"And can I give you one other tip, based on my deep love and respect for you?"

"Of course."

"Avoid the temptation to overshare."

* * *

The interrogation lasted two and a half hours and I feel I acquitted myself pretty well. The subsequent media coverage and analysis was relatively positive, suggesting that while we had committed some big mistakes for which we were going to be heavily fined, the business had put in place the appropriate levels of checks and controls and, more importantly, shown its remorse and contrition.

The session was intended to prove that ambitious tech businesses would do anything to hack growth but that in a climate of data manipulation for political ends, commercial success could not be at the expense of protecting individual privacy. Questioning focused on the dubious tactics that allowed us to use a supermarket loyalty scheme database and the appropriateness of our strategy, given that we were a brand that encouraged better parenting.

We had worked on countering these arguments. I stressed that we were guilty of initial overenthusiasm, that is all. We had supported our chief technical officer (Dimitri) but were too distracted by start-up mayhem to have scrutinised him fully. It was well-intentioned naivety, nothing more. I made it very clear that Dimitri was no longer with the company and a new puritanical regime was firmly in place. I also made a rather elaborate speech on the accidental nature of success. I explained that in truth we had started out as a marketplace for sellers and become, by chance, a major publishing house. All because I had bumped into my drunken old school friend. I actually got a few laughs with the story of my chance encounter with Nigel.

My point was that our elevation to a global digital platform resulted from events that were not part of our original business plan. This did not condone using data incorrectly, but should allow some tolerance for us as an organisation learning as we got bigger and putting in place the structures necessary to ensure the correct behaviour. 'No start-up can anticipate all the implications of its slim chance of success.'

Despite the rehearsal and the scenario-planning, I had one other point to make that I did not share in advance with anyone. Asked for a closing statement, I avoided the temptation for a rambling speech about the emotional journey we had undertaken and looked directly at the bank of colourless politicians, pausing with deliberate theatricality to make sure they were listening properly. They started to shuffle papers with irritation, which was not the response I was looking for.

"I now run PrimaParent as sole CEO. My co-founder left some months ago. I want to assure you all that the integrity and standards of this business will never be compromised again."

I leant back in my chair, rather pleased with myself, and waited for the sound of applause.

* * *

As the room cleared, I was overcome with a wave of exhaustion that seemed to be the product not just of the morning's interrogation but of the exertions of months of turbulence. My limbs felt like heavy weights I couldn't lift, and my head began to throb. Sarah and the bump gave me a congratulatory hug, while my parents hovered uncertainly next to her. My mother tried to lighten the mood by saying, "All things being equal, I think I enjoyed Judith meeting The Queen a bit more."

My father looked wistful. The debate had touched on many of the challenges of digital growth and social purpose on which he based most of his current writing. After what seemed like much deliberation, he crouched behind my chair and whispered, "Alex, you were brilliant today. You had principles. You said sorry. You were very strong."

Before I could revel in the praise, my phone, which I had turned back on, started to ping continuously like a demented heart monitor as messages came flooding in. They were complimentary and supportive, except for two.

Nigel had sent me a message that simply read: *Why would you tell Parliament I am a drunk? You're an arsehole.*

And then there was a message from Julian, who had disappeared into a celebrity lifestyle since his exit. I opened it with some dread.

Vengeance is Mine: I will repay. In due time their foot will slip; for their day of disaster is near, and their doom is coming quickly. Deuteronomy 32:35

25. End

The adrenaline that had sustained me for some weeks dried up and a few days later I took to bed with a very nasty bout of flu. Not some effete cough and runny nose, but a full-blooded roaring temperature and an inability to stay awake for very long. Hallucinating dreams and sweat-soaked tee shirts, I lay isolated in the spare bedroom. Even Sarah, fuelled by a GP's disdain for petty illness, showed me some sympathy and occasionally brought me paracetamol.

It took a week to recover, and when I returned to the office, I had an inexplicable sense of foreboding. Julian's note had made me paranoid that he was planning for something nasty to happen when I left the building at lunchtime to pick up a tuna baguette and yogurt. There was little time for irrational fear, as a few days out of the business and the mountain of tasks I faced had become positively Himalayan.

We were preparing the launch of Clyde Pilestone's final 'Reluctant Martian' novel, *End of Time*, and there were many problems. Nigel kept rewriting the ending, which meant it was proving extremely difficult to put in place a global launch plan. At the same time, the crippling expectation made his behaviour increasingly venomous. He wanted to approve everything and didn't want to be bothered by us continually trying to show him things. We had a team of hundreds of people around the world preparing for the event, unsure what to do to meet the complicated project timetables that had been constructed.

By now, the only channel of communication with Nigel was through his wife and agent, Kate. She was immune to his increasingly difficult behaviour and this made her uncompromising in dealing with us. If he didn't deliver, we would just have to think flexibly of a solution. If, however, we were perceived to have let them down, the vitriol and threats that came our way would reduce our organisation to collective tears. The most vicious language was normally reserved for me. Nigel would intermittently emerge from his creative exile to call me and shout a string of rarely connected obscenities, quasi-racial insults and consistent threats of physical violence.

The business was growing every day. PrimaParent Learn had tapped into the global madness of ambitious parents pushing children relentlessly to greater academic accomplishment and was rolling out rapidly across twenty-two global offices. Our publishing empire was also flourishing. We were now a magnet for authors of children's/teen literature and an entertainment brand in our own right. The original business of selling experiences and products was stable, but in hind-sight would not have made us into anything nearly so remarkable.

I had a punishing travel schedule planned, visiting key European markets, Singapore, Hong Kong and the US to prepare for the launch of Nigel's concluding book. We had a board meeting and a global morale-raising summit for senior leaders, as well as an off-site for the leadership team to discuss the future. It was therefore extremely debilitating to have to deal with a series of random incidents that contributed to the unravelling of these carefully constructed plans.

No sooner had I returned from my illness than I had to confront the accusation that I was lying about my complicity in the supermarket-data scandal. Sitting by my laptop reviewing my travel plans, my phone rang and, without looking properly, I took the call.

"Hi Alex. This is James Connor." James was the up-and-coming journalist who wrote the profile of Julian and myself for *The Times* that fomented the future conflict between me and my father. His career had taken off and he was a highly awarded writer, gleefully attacking the poor behaviour of corporations. He came straight to the point.

"I have heard from reliable sources that despite your declaration that you were completely unaware of the use of illegal hacked data, you were complicit in the decision for its use. Would you care to comment?" Given that it was Dimitri, Julian and myself who had the initial conversation about whether we should use it, and it would take an act of generosity to call Dimitri 'reliable', the culprit for this ambush could only have been Julian.

I wasn't going to make this easy, so I simply said: "James, I have no comment and have made my position very clear in everything I've said to date."

There followed the pantomime-like back-and-forth questioning of an aggressive journalist asking the same thing in slightly different ways, with me finding non-committal but increasingly irritable ways of refusing to give a definitive answer. This, of course, brought momentary respite but did not dissipate the threat.

The next day, *The Times* ran a relatively small story that cast just enough doubt about my position and suggested that there was more scandal to come. There followed a fair amount of media flak. My faux-loyal deputy, Clark, bombarded me with suggestions of how to deal with the renewed barrage of interest, supposedly worried for my well-being while maintaining the enthusiasm of someone sniffing personal opportunity.

As much as I tried to focus on running the organisation, more unexpected crises arose. The Information Commissioner's Office took an exceedingly dim view of the *Times* story and the need for a credible explanation intensified. Concurrently, the National Crime Agency reopened its investigation into whether criminal charges could be brought against me. They had discovered a former IT employee of the supermarket enjoying a disproportionately lavish lifestyle and wanted to chase the money trail, expecting it to lead to us.

There was further turmoil within our business. The MDs of our offices in NYC and Paris announced their resignations and intention to set up a rival business. Unbeknown to me, Greg Simpson and Amélie Fournier had forged a personal and professional *entente cordiale* at a global get-together, which came as disappointing news to their respective spouses. With the support of a mysterious backer, they announced that they intended to launch a rival education and parental advice business.

While not an existential threat, it was a major inconvenience. We needed to sort legal non-competes and restrictions to hinder their progress, which took time and effort. More irritatingly, we were losing two very strong operators for key markets at a crucial juncture. Still a youngish business, our succession planning was not really resolved across different offices to withstand such knocks. We had no one to replace them and as recruitment always takes time, I was going to have to get more involved in day-to-day operations than I wanted.

An even greater pressure was our own corporate future. We were locked in discussions with various institutions to determine whether we should have an IPO to fund our growth or bring in additional private investment. Moshe wanted to get to a resolution that would suit him and, as our chairman, he drove a lot of the conversations, sometimes with collegiate openness and other times with the furtive secrecy of a Cold War spy.

Nigel had made it clear that our 'Resilient Martian' money tap was going to be turned off as he focused his writing aspirations elsewhere. We knew we had to maximise the short-term uplift of the new book and then find some new ways to bring in the dosh. Being linked to scandal and intrigue was not helping and we were advised not to consider the IPO at this stage, because while our revenues and profitability were unusually impressive, our reliance on one primary source made the institutions question their sustainability.

Moshe was intent on realising some value or grabbing further control. He would phone me one day and tell me he wanted to buy me out. The next call, as if oblivious to the previous conversation, he would declare he'd had enough of the business and was taking steps to get out. True, he owned less, but his influence was disproportionate and, more importantly, he seemed to have control of the other shareholders.

George Dobson had gone missing in action. His Chinese business misfortunes meant that we never heard from him. Moshe made it clear that they had an informal agreement whereby he had George's proxy, which I found hard to believe but even harder to disprove. Brooke and Cole seemed to be focusing efforts elsewhere and her motivational messages were drying up. Brooke was particularly cross with me when she found out that the reports of the coaching Julian and I had received were fabricated. You didn't need Sherlock Holmes to pin the blame on Julian as the likely source once more.

It was very lonely dealing with it all. Affable enthusiasm, my primary mode of existence, was not enough to buy me any support or friendship from the board. Alice, my loyal acolyte, did not think like a warrior/politician/serial killer, which was what I needed to anticipate Moshe's next move. I felt extremely vulnerable.

It was strange to feel such a lack of control over something you have built and love dearly. Imagine you become a parent. You try to be the best father or mother on the planet. Then said child reaches early adulthood and you become a helpless observer to what happens next. Looking back, I was beginning to grieve for the loss of PrimaParent before it actually happened. I had been so driven for success that I never anticipated it could cope without me.

In the end, my own end was precipitated by spoiling someone else's ending.

* * *

Xargon 5 lay dying as the golden sun burnt an iridescent palette of yellow, gold and phosphorus white. The stars were dulled by impenetrable clouds of toxic gas released by the unstoppable implosion of the universe. Blackness, like a cosy blanket, began to engulf him, and as his spirit was released into the godless nothingness that now existed, his last thought was of his long-dead family. Loyal, kind and pure, they had been extinguished by the random cruelty of a civilisation lacking civility. As his eyes closed, his final sensation was the warmth of undiminished love. When we destroy everything, he realised, that is all that remains.

Cheery stuff. Nigel was clearly feeling particularly nihilistic when he decided that his hero had to perish in an existential rant against a venomous and indifferent world. His fan base loved the cheerful and brave hero who had travelled the galaxy to find the love of his wife and children. Their commitment to his well-being demanded that he should be reunited with his family, not snuff it because the folly of man had caused the destruction of the entire universe. It hurt your brain to think about the finality of everything, as described by grumpy Clyde Pilestone.

What made it far worse was that the final gloomy paragraph found itself posted on Facebook two weeks before the launch and was distributed with uncaring largesse through any social media channel or news outlet you could think of. Not a corner of the world (about to be destroyed in this book) was unaware of Xargon's fate.

One of the issues we had faced with Nigel was his refusal to tell us the ending. This was a pretty significant obstruction to developing a marketing strategy. He told us he was considering several options, ranging from a romcom resolution with snogging to a nuclear option of everyone dying because it was the end of the world. We suggested that the latter might not be good for business, as most people prefer a happy ending to Armageddon.

Contrary as ever, this impelled Nigel to make it two shades darker than bleak. He shared it with a limited group of us in secrecy and despite our pleas to consider an alternative, the more we protested, the more obdurate he became. We kept warning him it was a monumental slap in the face to his devoted fans. This seemed to please him.

I never discovered how it got out. Our systems were well protected (thanks to Moshe's constant intervention) so it could only have been a leak from a limited number of people with access to the manuscript. Maybe thirty over the period of a month, across our office? There was no evidence of incriminating emails or other messaging. Someone must have gone old-school and written it up by hand and snuck it out. Even the source of the Facebook post was impossible to trace.

When it posted, there was mayhem. '*Is this true?*' was the first question that appeared in the media, and if so, how would it affect the sales of the book now that the ending was known? There was also much comment about the publishing ineptitude of everyone at PrimaParent to allow the ending of its prize asset to be ruined. As for the fans, there were petitions and forums dedicated to their betrayal by the ending of a novel they had not read. You can't kill Superman or Batman. Xargon 5 deserved similar immortality.

'Incandescence' would be a mild description of the emotion that came my way from Nigel. He peppered me with incessant text messages for several days but with a concentration of unpleasantness focused on the late night to obliterate any prospect of sleep. When I tried to speak to him, I was confronted by a tirade of angry and disconnected insults. Rather than simply apologise, I attempted to create a case for there being some positivity to be gleaned from the incident.

"We may not have meant to start this debate, but I think we've created a disproportionate level of interest," I boldly stated on one midnight call.

"You are a moron. How many different ways can I say it? Of course it could be good for the book. But what we are debating is your incompetence and there is little ambiguity on that subject. You are a corporate pygmy. A Lilliputian digital dork. Need I go on?"

"Oh, I'm sure you have a few more obscure insults that you'd like to take me through. Do you have an app that generates them?"

"No, Lazarus. Your ineptitude stimulates my spontaneity." And with that, he hung up.

Kate was more measured in her anger. A barrage of letters arrived with the threat of imminent litigation and the severing of our relationship. Nothing could be done while the book was being launched, but legal jihad was very much in the offing. As it happened, the leak did not affect its critical reception. The question of whether franchised entertainment needed always to be upbeat swung in Nigel's favour. They loved his decision to demonstrate that the fragility of existence could only be offset by the constancy of love. When the book was reviewed, it was almost universally revered as a brilliant conclusion to a thought-provoking series. Nigel was thrilled, I'm sure. If there was one thing he truly loved above any form of commercial success, it was praise.

The furore, in the end, probably lost a few percentage points of sales. After several weeks, it had performed strongly, but not quite as well as its predecessor. We could never confirm the impact of the leak on its financial performance. But that was not the point from our perspective. Publishers preserve the secrecy of their authors' works. We were seen once more as naive ingénues, not literary heavyweights.

There was one final assault coming my way. James Connor, who had never been that impressed since interviewing me and Julian, refused to let go of my alleged complicity in stealing data that wasn't mine and then lying to a bunch of overzealous politicians. Unfortunately, I kept inadvertently giving him ammunition with which he could destroy my reputation.

For several weeks, I became aware via our press office that he was sniffing around for intelligence not just on my poor decisions but also my style of leadership, values and seeming total lack of integrity or moral fibre. Every few days, I would receive a call or message from someone within or related to the business, telling me they had been hounded by a persistent journalist with some very specific questions about me. I realised with mounting dread that he was only speaking with people who had some vestige of loyalty. Imagine what someone with a grudge might say, and how unlikely it was that they'd tip me off.

I did not have to wait too long for the answer. He rang me one Saturday to say he had written an article for the *Sunday Times*. He outlined its content and asked me if I had a final comment to make. My world was imploding like the universe at the end of Clyde Pilestone's final novel. Wearily, I conceded to my journalistic nemesis:

"Our promise has always been 'Family First'. You have to remember that my aspiration has always been to create something of value to a diverse audience. We want happy parents and children enjoying their interactions with us. We also want happy people working at PrimaParent to deliver this vision. I will let others judge how well I have done."

* * *

At midnight, I downloaded *the Sunday Times* from my app. The headline eviscerated any lingering hope that it would be a favourable account of my well-intentioned efforts:

DISHONESTY AND INCOMPETENCE DESTROY
PRIMAPARENT'S UNICORN ASPIRATIONS

I was the focus of the article and my achievements were dissected with surgical precision. Dimitri was quoted extensively ('a former high-level tech leader') and Nigel's invective given free rein, although denuded of swear words ('I remember Alex at school. Unpopular. Unimaginative. Unremarkable.')

The article was based on very specific details, including being mocked at a company conference, allowing a weak FD to get the numbers wrong until I was made to fire him, and being a walking PR disaster on many occasions. It revealed that after being dismissed by the board, I brought in my ex-partner's vengeful ex-wife to unethically save myself. Most alarming was the revelation that I had known all about the dubious provenance of much of the data we used for initial growth hacking. When subsequently cornered, I had proved myself very adept at lying – to regulators and politicians, you name it. Pinocchio had nothing on me.

Julian was not quoted. He didn't need to be. The detail he had provided for the article was highly specific and completely damning. His vengeance had been delivered through a series of anonymous tip-offs. He must have had a ball.

The article concluded with my quote about letting the reader decide if our vision had been delivered. James Connor felt the question needed resolution, so he added:

Evidence would point to ambition clouding Alex Lazarus's judgement. A warning for those seeking glory at all costs.

I sat in the kitchen with a cup of tea, having told Sarah that I wanted to be alone. She couldn't have looked more worried as she trudged up the stairs, not ideal for someone who was due to have a baby in ten days. After an eternity of quiet contemplation in the still night, my phone pinged in rapid succession.

The first message was from my father: *You do not deserve this, Alex. You have really achieved something.*

The second one was from Moshe. It simply said: *Alex, we need to talk. Immediately.*

For some unfathomable reason, he had even added a smiley face emoticon.

Epilogue

Moshe fired me the next day.

It was a brief meeting. Once again, I ascended to the minimalist white hotel suite. I nodded to his security man, who I knew well, and for a moment considered asking him to intervene on my behalf. Moshe was flanked by his lawyer and, to my horror, the irrepressibly cheerful super-smug Clark Templeton. Moshe did not offer coffee or make any attempt at preamble but stared at me with cold, unblinking eyes, and then gave an expansive sigh that seemed to connote enormous disappointment.

"Well, *habibi*, we have come to the end of your bumpy ride." I knew I had walked into my own execution, so I decided that petulant silence was the required mature tactic. He couldn't have cared less and seemed keen to get through the conversation quickly so he could get on with some proper work.

"Alex, you have lost the backing of not just the board but of most of the company. It has been one mistake after another, and you are driving us backwards. You should actually thank Clark for his intervention."

"What intervention?" Silence was no longer an option and I angrily clenched my fists, which I suspect just made me look silly.

"Clark has done a lot of damage limitation with Kate to protect our future commercial relationship with Clyde Pilestone."

"Has he now?" Silly phrases were unfortunately flying out of my mouth. A measured response was beyond me.

"We may be able to preserve the relationship, but your school friend Nigel will only allow it if you are nowhere near the business. He couldn't have been clearer."

Clark now felt the unsolicited need to make an impressively irritating contribution. "He can be quite hurtful and personal, can't he? And sometimes it's hard to follow his language, which seems a bit old-fashioned."

By now I was straining to preserve any vestige of dignity, wanting to cry, scream and stamp my little feet. I had to refrain from responding; having entered the room calmly, I intended to exit the same way. Instead, I turned to the lawyer, an unfamiliar American who had sat impassively throughout.

"So, tell me, what is Moshe proposing?" It was time to retreat to the safety of my own lawyer to scrutinise any offer made. Everyone seemed relieved I wasn't frothing at the mouth, and she pulled a manila envelope from her bag and almost tossed it dismissively in my direction.

"The good news about our proposal is you keep your shares unchallenged, but the even better news is we have made a proposal to buy them from you. It is time-sensitive, however. Moshe is being very generous. You have forty-eight hours from today to decide."

At that point, Moshe's phone rang, and he got up to take the call, dismissing me with a casual wave of farewell as he moved on to an Alex-free future. The injustice of being ousted by the person meant to support me felt very cruel. Indeed, if I had any doubt about his swaggering indifference, he emphasised the point by inviting my successor to witness my dismissal.

I got up, fully intending to leave in cold silence. Unfortunately, Clark extended his hand towards me with a condescending suggestion of 'no hard feelings'. My feelings were actually hardening by the second, so I let him hold his hand out for several seconds, shook my head and walked away. Sadly, my graceful exit was ruined by tripping over the corner of a coffee table and stumbling a few steps with flailing arms, before correcting myself and trying to pretend it had not happened. As I closed the door behind me, Clark was smirking. If only there had been a baseball bat handy.

* * *

Two days later, Sarah went into labour. She had been late with the other two and this time was a week early. It wasn't that we were unprepared, rather that I had hoped to make the biggest decision of my life undistracted. Instead, I found myself in hospital with a poor signal, trying to send emails between contractions. Moshe had offered to buy me out for half the value of my shares. We had spent a lot of time having the company valued when considering the IPO, and while we hadn't quite made it to unicorn status (unless it was a two-legged wingless unicorn), we were doing pretty well when you consider we had only been going five years.

His offer letter was short and very clear. Moshe wanted to do the deal immediately but argued that my recent wayward performance at the helm had devalued the company significantly. Therefore, he was prepared to offer me an amount equating to half of the most recent valuation (actually 48.945 per cent), a robust sum of cash sitting in an offshore bank somewhere, waiting to be transferred into my account. I had two days to decide, as a protracted negotiation could impact further on the fortunes of the business.

I should say that we are talking an enormous life-changing dollop of cash, an amount equivalent to a hefty lottery win. A sum so unfathomably large that a life of sports-car driving, exotic holidaying and general indolence beckoned. Work would be a distant memory and my children would want for nothing, hideously overindulged in the process. It may be difficult, therefore, to feel sympathy for my self-indulgence at this juncture. All that personal wealth, simply by selling my shares on the cheap.

PrimaParent was going to make me very rich indeed, but it was accompanied by a strong need for recognition and affirmation. I had created something globally significant from a casual conversation. Why wasn't lots of money in my bank account enough?

As a child, I had been in awe of my grandfather's anecdotes about his commercial wiliness, triumphing over any puny adversary he encountered. Despite many accolades, I suffered from a sense of inadequacy that I was just the bloke who founded the company, not the genius behind its success. A chance encounter delivered us Clyde Pilestone, Julian's commercial flair secured its commercial benefits, Moshe's ruthless control kept us on track, and the exciting subsequent innovation stemmed from Clark. *Alex Lazarus? Nice chap. Full of ideas, but all over the shop in reality.*

My pride and self-esteem were deflated by an offer suggesting I was only half the business genius I thought I was. It didn't help that my advisors kept telling me forcefully it was a ploy I had to ignore. Moshe wanted to do a quick deal because he had some plan that my continued presence could only undermine. I was now a blockage that needed to be cleared.

I found myself in a negotiation, unable to get past the grief and wounded ego and totally alone as Sarah was not really in the mood to chat. As the emails from my lawyers cluttered my inbox, all suggesting delaying tactics to up the value of the offer, I couldn't stop thinking that something I loved was dying, just as a new precious family member was about to be born.

I'm sure Moshe did not think so poetically. Maybe I was too sensitive for my own good, or just very tired. I had no doubt that it was a trap and was sufficiently self-aware to know I would find it hard to separate myself emotionally from the business if I left. I'd need for it to flounder without me.

Sarah's labour started slowly, and I sat next to her or walked around the hospital holding her hand, spewing out half-hearted phrases of encouragement as I tried to bring order to my fragmented thoughts. (*You've got this, Sarah. Remember to breathe, Sarah. Fancy a KitKat, Sarah?*) As the day wore on and her pain increased, something told me there was only one way forward. When we moved to the pushing-the-baby-out bit at the end, I grew certain of the right decision.

At 11.53 p.m. on a Tuesday night, my son Max was born. He filled his lungs with air and bawled with angry gusto, maybe in disappointment at meeting me. There were seven minutes left until Moshe's deadline passed. The midwife congratulated me, and I thanked Sarah for just being perfect.

In an office in the West End, a group of lawyers were sitting in a conference room surrounded by the sad leftover cartons of a Chinese takeaway, drinking cold coffee and impatiently awaiting my call. Holding Sarah's hand and staring at my son, I somehow managed to dial in to them, and in a voice that had never felt more certain, I quietly said:

"Please call Moshe and sell my shares."

* * *

The lawyers drafted the paperwork over the next few days and I made one non-negotiable stipulation. Moshe had to offer to buy Alice's shares too. I had spoken to her throughout the process and she had been her normal steadfast, robustly honest self when I told her I'd been fired.

"Duh. Do you think they didn't phone me to tell me it was going to happen? I am a shareholder, you know, and CEOs are always getting fired in this place. I think it unlikely you're going to get reinstated this time."

"I think that's a realistic assumption. What did you tell them?"

"I said I would have to consider my position too. You know how it goes. I can't work, if working is without you."

"Oh, don't be mad. You don't need to do anything rash on my behalf. You've worked too hard for the business to leave in a huff. You'll be better off without me to annoy you."

"That's very sweet, but I think that if I have to report in to Clark, I may end up murdering him to avoid listening to any more clichés. Do you know, he actually said to me last week: 'Remember Alice, it is always darkest under the lighthouse.'"

"Think carefully. That's all I ask."

"Alex, you have to get me out, there's no debate. I trust you completely. How sad is that?"

As it happens, it proved very simple to get her bought out and she became instantaneously a very wealthy woman who, like me, could choose a different way to live. Moshe wanted as much control as he could get, so it evidently suited him to acquiesce. And a lawyer-filled week or so later, we were both no longer shareholders in the business we had created.

The confirmatory call came through to me at a moment of family celebration. It was actually my son's 'brit milah', his circumcision, when the sale money was transferred. Thousands of years ago, Abraham made a covenant with God. Circumcising Isaac, his son, and ensuring the continuity of this command, conferred on him the promise of land and greatness. Loyalty and devotion, faith and duty could bring great rewards. How fitting that this archaic tradition was performed the same day I relinquished control of a professional life devoted to parenting.

The ceremony is mercifully quick and afterwards Max slept soundly, grumbling occasionally at the indignity of his recent surgery. I felt tired, sad and drained. It was over now, and I had to work out what to do next. My emotions were more volatile than usual, and I was quite tearful. We had family and a few friends over to celebrate and I slumped morosely on the sofa. My father sat next to me and handed me a cup of strong coffee. After a minute or two, he turned to me and smiled.

"Well, you are now, I believe, what they call in capitalist circles a multi-millionaire. More money in your account than the GDP of most of Latin America. No need to work. All that time to spend with us. How does it feel?"

I turned my head to him and smiled weakly. "I enjoyed the bit where I trampled over the poor people. That felt nice."

"You'll be buying your old Ma and Pa a nice seaside place somewhere, surely. You know how fond we are of the French Riviera."

"For sure. I'm looking at caravan parks as we speak. I'll even get you one with running water."

"And I have every intention of turning you into a case history I can teach undergraduates. I think I'll call it 'The pitfalls of chasing the digital dollar'."

"I might enrol myself. Have you got anything nice to say, Dad?"

He put his arm around my shoulders and drew me towards him, giving me a kiss on the top of my head in the process.

"Oh yes, for sure, Alex. Zayde would be so proud of you. So proud. Spend it wisely, son."

* * *

A couple of days later, Clark was announced in the role of CEO of PrimaParent. The press release thanked me for my incredible contribution as founder and looked to a bright future under Clark's stewardship. His achievements were effusively spelt out and the elevation was accompanied by some other news. In addition to continued exclusive rights to the 'Resilient Martian' series, Nigel

O'Connor had agreed to let PrimaParent publish his next series of novels. ('Sabre of Truth' – the tale of Caleb Clyne, an eighteenth-century revolutionary swordsman available to the highest bidder.) There had clearly been many conversations with Nigel and Kate from which I had been excluded.

PrimaParent Holidays was also launched. There wasn't much ground left to cover for helping improve the quality of family life, but I didn't expect this to be part of the release. A few weeks previously, when I was still CEO, we were working on the business model for roll-out the following year. There is no way it could have been ready. Rather, Moshe was controlling the narrative to beef up the performance of the business. Now that he had hoovered up my shares on the cheap, it was time to raise the stated value of Prima-Parent to the outside world.

Even more miraculously, the Information Commissioner resolved their outstanding investigation with a £100,000 toothless fine. Much of their conclusion was focused on the 'board's excision of previous management responsible for unchecked and inappropriate behaviour'. I was a convenient scapegoat, it seemed. I could never prove it, but somehow Moshe's data-security network was a useful ally to them and it would not have surprised me if somehow Avi Ram had been instructed by his boss to support the information police across the world in return for them turning a blind eye.

I did get many calls from people sad to see me go and the messages were kind and emotional. I had lots of loyal friends in the business, but there was little evidence that they thought my departure would bring the company crashing down around them. Liked and respected maybe, but ultimately totally replaceable.

I spent the next few months getting on with my domestic life in as low-key a fashion as possible. My body ached with corporate weariness. Everyone advised me to decompress and free my mind from considering my future. I did decide to try to trim my flabby tummy and look after myself better. Five years from launch and my man boobs were so big, you'd think it was me breastfeeding baby Max.

Sarah was so happy to have me home to hang out with quietly, enjoying the chaos and exhaustion of a new baby. We drank lots of tea and went for walks. Our horizons were limited to the practical considerations of naps and feeds. Days blurred into each other and I drifted aimlessly, with little purpose. I can't tell if it was a happy time. It was just different, fuelled by domestic contentment and professional grief.

One morning, I was distractedly giving the older two breakfast and reading *The Times* when I suddenly saw a headline that made me crash back into my former world. The fairy-tale romance between Lucy and Julian had progressed to an imminent fairy-tale wedding. What particularly piqued my interest was a quote from Julian, who declared: 'I recently had some great news professionally and it just seemed the right time to ask Lucy.'

My paranoid alter ego returned. What was the good news? Was he suffering less than me? Had he finally run out of stories to leak about me in revenge? I showed Sarah the article and she snorted in derision. "People like Julian always come out on top. They're just not afraid of the selfish consequences of their actions."

I thought this was a bit harsh – after all, he was entitled to remarry and Lucy was objectively quite a catch. I made this point to Sarah, who was too tired to argue, simply shrugging her shoulders and saying, "You may be right, but when all's said and done, you have to admit he's a bit of a wanker."

His ears must have been burning because the following day I got a text from him. It was a simple entreaty: *Bury the hatchet breakfast? Can you meet me at Manuela's tomorrow?*

* * *

Manuela's had not changed much, but perhaps looked a little tired and sorry for itself. When I arrived, there were a few tables with a single occupant on each. They were wearing headphones and tapping assiduously on laptops, nursing the dregs of a single cup of coffee with no visible signs of any food. No wonder Manuela's was struggling – they were not smashing enough avocados. Entrepreneurial opportunists using it as cheap office space was not a sustainable business model for an ambitious café.

Julian was already there, sitting, of course, at the table where we wrote our business plan a lifetime ago. He stood up as I approached and went to give me a hug of friendship, which was not what I expected. I had deliberated hard on whether to come. The last communication I had with him was a threat of biblical-proportion revenge. He had gone some way to achieving it, so I was unsure if acquiescing to a meeting was desirable. It was an opportunity to 'seek closure', but in practical terms I was not sure what that meant. I declined his attempted embrace.

"Sorry, Julian, I'm not sure I'm ready for displays of physical affection yet."

"Fair enough. We'll hold back on the cuddles until we finish."

The waitress came to take our order and I asked for a coffee. Despite being starving, I didn't want to order food in case I needed to sprint for the door. Julian had no such reservations and ordered something cooked. He could not have looked more relaxed. I decided that we needed to ease ourselves into the awkward stuff, so I kicked off with a bit of general chit-chat about his forthcoming marriage.

Despite Sarah's unwavering belief in his callousness, he could not have come across as more in love. He spoke briefly about Lucy and how considerate she was to his parenting responsibilities. His kids adored her. She was a kind and empathetic stepmum and he talked genuinely about planning to have more children with her. Inevitably, being the perennial romantic, I softened and told him how pleased I was that he had found such happiness. It was soon time to tackle the unspoken enmity.

"You really were vicious to me, Julian, when you left. My view was that our relationship was untenable and one of us had to go. After that, everywhere I looked, you were leaking bits of info and undermining me wherever you could. You were like the Russians trying to influence an election with fake news."

"It wasn't such fake news, though, was it? If you could trounce my reputation by getting rid of me, there was no way I was going to let you appear the patron saint of ethical behaviour."

"My question is why you could never accept that we were in this together. I always felt that you were trying to come across as the clever one behind the success. You loved it when something made me look silly."

"Alex, are you joking?"

"I think the amount we've both spent on lawyers over the last year would suggest that there is little that's funny about all this."

'It's remarkable how unaware you are of what it was like for me to be your partner."

"How so? I would pride myself that I'm lovely."

"Oh, there's no doubt that you're a top chap. Really good values, even-tempered, love your family. I don't know what you were trying to prove and to whom, but you were always obsessed with telling everyone it was your idea, not mine."

"Well, it was."

"But why would that matter? You felt that leadership meant telling everyone what you had achieved rather than sharing the load with the rest of us."

"I think you're being unfair?"

"Am I? This is not a case of who said what to whom. Trust me, even your closest confidants struggled to stop you making all of it about proving yourself to the world."

"Then why did you always put me down or ridicule me when you could?"

"Sometimes for sport, sometimes because I can be a bit nasty, but most of the time to stop your inane need to create a narrative about your ambition and your tedious journey of self-discovery."

I didn't know what to say. Maybe Julian was right. I could only see him as an obstacle to the vision I had created. He was no angel, but it was certainly much easier to amplify his faults and make them threats. I hadn't come to meet him for a moment of cathartic revelation, but his calm reasonableness was very unsettling. We were both out of the business now, so perhaps the therapy session could stop. I didn't want to hear more in case I ended up agreeing with him rather than making him the focal point of my anger.

"Let's leave it there. The noble thing would be to shake and remember the good times and the successes. We don't have to be friends but let's be proud of what we did." I extended my hand towards him and he clasped it in both of his and said nothing other than gently nodding.

"Anyway, Julian," I continued, "I learnt in the paper that you were getting married because you'd had some good business news. What is it?"

"Hadn't you heard? I sold our shares to Moshe." My heart danced a rumba as I saw the triumphant glint in his eye. "Yes, he wants complete control. Couldn't have been more enthusiastic to pick them up. Of course, you leaving the business was very helpful."

"How so?"

"The value of the company is soaring. I don't want to brag, but he paid me a lot more than you got. Made up for all the trouble you caused me with Catherine. We're actually on better terms now, you know?"

"And I assume that's the real reason we're meeting today? Not because you wanted to give me some meaningful insight into my behaviour?"

"What can I say? I'm very competitive, and you know how I hate to lose."

* * *

It has been six months since I met with Julian.

I have the perspective of distance and have managed to regain a smidgen of equilibrium. I am a stone lighter and go for a run every day. I sleep soundly and for once the children have a father who is genuinely attentive rather than distracted and guilt-ridden. Sarah has gone back to work and been made a partner at her practice. She has taken on the additional responsibility with measured calm and minimum fuss. I hope the kids have her genes.

My relationship with my parents is healthy. My father teases me for my wealth, and I try not to rise to the bait. He has even created a few university lecturing opportunities for me in his faculty. Half the undergraduates see me as a role model for self-advancement and success. Those with a social conscience question my need for so much wealth.

I've worked with my sister to do something worthwhile with my money and we've set up a charitable foundation focusing on vulnerable children. We are now being inundated with approaches and have hired a director to oversee the grant-giving. I had hoped it would be Judith, but she's moving to New York to take up her role in the Secretary-General's team at the UN, overseeing prevention of violence against children. We are all very proud and, as ever, she makes me look so shallow.

Alice called me a few months after we both left to tell me that her wife, Caroline, had been diagnosed with breast cancer. They had just come back from Tuscany, where they were looking to buy a wreck of a farmhouse to take on as a project. The prognosis was not a bad one for Caroline, but Alice went to pieces. I went to meet her immediately and watched as she silently wept in anger. She couldn't believe the cruelty of the timing.

"You sacrifice everything for your work because you have a vision of a better life for your family and then what? You get an enormous cheque followed by a shitty cancer diagnosis."

It was so cruel, as no one deserved unchallenged happiness as much as Alice. You should be able to work hard and enjoy the spoils, but unknown cosmic forces beg to differ. Should we live in the moment? Must we balance the hard work with a commitment not to compromise on our personal well-being? Maybe the universe is just random in its dispensation of good fortune. Alice and Caroline were stoic in their misfortune. As the tears and shock evaporated, they tackled the crisis with admirable calm. Caroline is coming through the treatment very well and somehow I know they'll be all right.

Dimitri has disappeared and I am secretly relieved. He is probably sitting in a dark cellar with super-fast broadband, working for different businesses in a highly illegal but effective fashion. I was very nice to him and he was a disloyal weirdo in the end.

Julian's wedding on Mykonos was covered extensively. Hollywood royalty, pop star royalty and real royalty all mingled in the glorious Aegean sunshine. There wasn't an ugly person in sight. Shortly afterwards, he announced he was launching his own talent agency. He would represent the interests of his wife and her coterie of acting friends, writers and directors. The press release also revealed that he had set up a joint venture with Nigel O'Connor to handle all of his future novels. (I had no interest in renewing any contact with Nigel, for what it's worth. He'd have to find some other schmuck to abuse with classically alliterative insults.)

After some soul-searching, I decided that a good person acknowledges the progress of others. Besides, I also wanted to be invited to some good premieres and parties. After a few days, I sent him a congratulatory text. It simply said: *Don't forget I made you what you are. I want 15% of everything.*

Brooke and Cole Johnson announced they were divorcing. I did some online investigation and saw much speculation about Brooke and her youthful yoga instructor breaking the normal acceptable boundaries of the teacher/pupil relationship. Nevertheless, a carefully crafted statement emphasised the amicable nature of their parting while stressing the continuation of their flourishing commercial partnership and shared financial investments.

Several weeks later Moshe bought them, George and everyone else out of PrimaParent. I was certainly not surprised but it was a big story, the Israeli cyber-security tycoon taking full control over a huge retail, entertainment and experience global brand. I can't really tell you his motivations, and the press struggled to link his core business protecting financial services and defence industries from hackers with a mainstream consumer organisation.

I was bombarded for comment and my least favourite journalist, James Connor, desperately sought an off-the-record conversation, which I refused. Having been the victim of leaked information and consistent character assaults in the press, I had no desire to do the same to Moshe. Besides, I'd met his muscular security team.

I can't tell you what Moshe's thinking was or what ambition drove him. I just knew that he always wanted to challenge, disrupt and surprise the world. He enjoyed making people uncomfortable, especially me. He had grown up on a kibbutz, a socialist experiment in ensuring that a principled and decent community spirit created something noble and worthwhile. Moshe liked power and the trappings of wealth and there is no psychological reason that explains his motivation. Sometimes people are driven because they know no other way to live. I have no doubt he will sell PrimaParent one day for much more money than he paid to gain control. And like a serial philanderer, he will then move on to his next conquest.

And what of me?

When Moshe bought PrimaParent, I felt a detached pride, but little jealousy or anger. I had put all my energy into its creation and had revelled in its success. But when I reflect on the intervening years, I can't really decide if I was happy. At heart, I have lots of ideas and want everyone to love me, but I also like the mundane nature of everyday life and the occasional midweek trip to the cinema, making sure I also never forget the sanctity of a happy family.

As for ambition, perhaps my father was right all those years ago when he argued with my grandfather. There is an inquisitive side to me that is interested in simply having a good brain and using it for something other than making money. I am curious. I love words. I have always wanted to write a book.

So that is what I am sitting down to do right now.

Acknowledgements

This book has an autobiographical seed.

On a hot summer's day in 1999, my very close friend Maurice Helfgott and I were loosely supervising our two-year-old children in the playground in Queen's Park as our heavily pregnant wives relaxed in an adjacent café. He was a rising star at M&S, and I was forging ahead with my advertising career, producing mediocre yogurt and toilet paper commercials. Mindful of the exploding dotcom revolution, we brainstormed our future millions and alighted on the concept of *fabparent.com,* which was going to be a global marketplace of solutions for over-stressed parents. Over the following few weeks, we met up and hatched loose ideas for a business plan to precipitate a digital parenting revolution. However, our second children were born, and we were engulfed by practical childcare responsibilities. The imaginary start-up wound down; Maurice was put in charge of a sizeable dotcom investment fund for M&S, and I got a decent pay rise when I moved to another agency.

For years we always joked about *what if* and imagined a different reality. At the end of 2018, lying in the bath trying to imagine my next attempt at a first novel, I wondered what success might have looked like had we had the confidence to take such a risky step, and the germ of a business idea became the inspiration for this novel. I must stress that while Alex may have inherited some of my more grating personality traits, Julian Lloyd-Mason is an entirely fictitious creation. Maurice has been the best of friends and we have managed to share some entrepreneurial journeys together subsequently. His unstinting encouragement and enthusiasm for this book has really inspired me.

Three books have been very useful to guide the narrative. William Casey King's 2013 book *Ambition, A History: From Vice to Virtue* (Yale University Press) is a great study of the profound changes in the meaning of 'ambition' from Elizabethan England to the Declaration of Independence. To understand the mercurial mayhem of a start-up business, I found Brad Stone's 2017 *The Upstarts* (Corgi) and John Carreyrou's *2018 Bad Blood* (Picador) enormously helpful. The former charts the rise of Airbnb and Uber, while the latter is the astonishing tale of Elizabeth Holmes and the Theranos scandal. They both prove that ambition can often be driven by luck, unrelenting drive and a flexible vision aligned to questionable morality. These bonkers start-up stories liberated me to create my own unlikely narrative.

Huge thanks to John, George, Nikki, Kelly, Gabrielle and the team at whitefox for training this enthusiastic puppy and all the wise guidance and advice throughout. And thanks to Jack Smyth for designing a terrific cover.

And finally, to my gorgeous wife Hannah, as we approach our 30th wedding anniversary, my eternal thanks for all the love and support which has seen us metaphorically grow from an ambitious start-up into a secure and established corporation. You laughed at all the supposed funny lines I shouted to you as I wrote. And let's be honest, it's not as if you haven't heard them before!

March 2021